POCKET POSTERS

GCSE
Physics
Revision Guide

Improving understanding
through colour and clarity

Get your FREE digital book!

This book includes a free digital edition for use on
computers (PC and Mac), tablets or smartphones.

Go to ddedu.co.uk/phys
and enter this code...

TVQqcjYCv

GCSE Physics

Contents

Energy Stores & Systems

Energy Stores

Energy cannot be created or destroyed. It can only be transferred or transformed from one energy store to another. Energy is measured in joules (J). There are many different energy stores, including:

 M *Magnetic*

 **G** *Gravitational potential*

E *Electrostatic*

T *Thermal*

 N *Nuclear*

 E *Elastic potential*

C *Chemical*

 K *Kinetic*

Light, sound and electricity are NOT stores of energy.
They are ways of transferring energy from one store to another.

Energy Transfer

Energy is stored in different systems (an object or group of objects), and when a system changes, energy can be transferred by:

| Heating | Work done by forces | Work done when a current flows | Radiation |

Examples of Energy Transfer in Systems

1 When an electric kettle is switched on, the water gets hotter. There is now more thermal energy (or internal energy) stored in the hot water than there was when it was cold. Energy has been transferred by electricity (work done when a current flows) and heating.

2 When a moving object hits an obstacle, some of its store of **kinetic energy** is transferred into different energy stores in the obstacle. If the obstacle breaks, each broken piece will carry some of the **kinetic energy** away. If the obstacle does not break, then some of the kinetic energy from the object will likely be transferred into **thermal energy** in the object and the obstacle.

3 When someone throws a ball, chemical energy in the person's arm is transferred to the kinetic energy store of the ball and the arm. Energy has been transferred mechanically by work done by forces.

4 When a vehicle brakes, the kinetic energy store in the car wheel is transferred to the thermal energy store of the brakes. Energy has been transferred by work done against the force of friction. For example, Formula One cars brake at such high speeds that they must be specifically designed to withstand high temperatures.

daydream EDUCATION

Calculating Energy Stores

The amount of energy in some of the most common energy stores can be calculated using the following formulae.

Kinetic Energy Stores

A moving object has a store of kinetic energy. When an object speeds up, energy is transferred into the store; when it slows down, energy is transferred out. The greater the mass and speed of the object, the greater its store of kinetic energy.

joules (J) kilograms (kg)

kinetic energy = 0.5 × mass × (speed)²

$$[E_k = \frac{1}{2} m v^2]$$

metres per second (m/s)

A car is travelling at a speed of 30 m/s and has a mass of 1,200 kg. Calculate the kinetic energy of the car.

Kinetic energy = 0.5 × mass × (speed)²
= 0.5 × 1,200 × (30)²
= 0.5 × 1,200 × 900
= 540,000 J or 540 kJ

Gravitational Potential Energy (GPE) Stores

An object raised above ground level has a store of GPE. The greater the strength of the gravitational field and the height and mass of the object, the greater its store of GPE. The gravitational field at the Earth's surface produces a force of approximately 9.8 N/kg. This means that an object with a mass of 1 kg is attracted towards the centre of the Earth by a force of 9.8 N.

joules (J) kilograms (kg) metres (m)

GPE = mass × gravitational field strength × height

$$[E_p = m g h]$$

newtons per kilogram (N/kg)

A crane raises a crate to a height of 15 m. It has gained 22,500 J of GPE. Calculate the mass of the crate.

GPE = mass × gravitational field strength × height

$$mass = \frac{GPE}{gravitational\ field\ strength \times height}$$

$$= \frac{22,500}{9.8 \times 15}$$

= 153 kg (3 s.f.)

Rearrange the equation to make mass the subject.

Elastic Potential Energy Stores

A squashed or stretched object has a store of elastic potential energy. The more an object is stretched or squashed, the greater its store of elastic potential energy – as long as the object has not exceeded its limit of proportionality.

joules (J) newtons per metre (N/m)

elastic potential energy = 0.5 × spring constant × (extension)²

$$[E_e = \frac{1}{2} k e^2]$$

metres (m)

A spring with a spring constant of 50 N/m is extended by 8 cm. Calculate the elastic potential energy stored in the spring.

elastic potential energy = 0.5 × spring constant × (extension)²
= 0.5 × 50 × (0.08)²
= 0.16 J

8 cm = 0.08 m

daydream EDUCATION

Work Done & Power

A force is a push or pull that acts on an object. Work is done when a force acts on an object causing the object to move a distance in the direction of the force.

Work done can be calculated using the following equation:

joules (J)   newtons (N)   metres (m)

work = force × distance moved in the direction of the force

$$[W = F s]$$

Power is defined as the rate at which work is done on an object or the rate at which energy is transferred from one energy store to one or more energy stores.

watts (W)   joules (J)   watts (W)   joules (J)

$$power = \frac{energy\ transferred}{time}$$

$$[P = \frac{E}{t}]$$

OR

$$power = \frac{work\ done}{time}$$

$$[P = \frac{W}{t}]$$

seconds (s)   seconds (s)

An energy transfer of 1 joule per second is equal to 1 watt of power.

Example

If one crane can lift a container more quickly than another crane lifting the same object, we say it is more powerful because it is transferring energy (or doing work) more quickly.

It takes 9000 J of work to lift a crate to the top of a tower. Motor A can lift the crate into place in 50 s. Motor B can do the same job in 60 s. Calculate the power of the two motors.

Motor A

$$power\ of\ motor\ A = \frac{work\ done}{time}$$

$$= \frac{9000}{50}$$

$$= 180\ W$$

Motor B

$$power\ of\ motor\ B = \frac{work\ done}{time}$$

$$= \frac{9000}{60}$$

$$= 150\ W$$

Motor A has transferred the same amount of energy as motor B, but it has done it in less time. The energy is now stored as gravitational potential energy.

daydream EDUCATION

Energy Transfer & Efficiency

Energy can be transferred from one store to another, but it cannot be destroyed or created.

Energy Transfer

When there are energy transfers in a closed system, there is no net change in the total energy. However, some of the energy is dissipated or 'wasted', and is stored in less useful ways.

A **Sankey diagram** is often used to display the transfer of input energy into its useful and wasted outputs. It is drawn to scale, and the width of each arrow shows the amounts of energy involved. The length of the arrows has no significance.

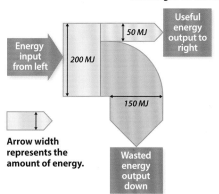

Energy input from left

200 MJ

50 MJ — Useful energy output to right

150 MJ

Arrow width represents the amount of energy.

Wasted energy output down

Car Engine

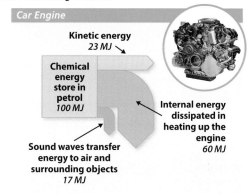

Kinetic energy
23 MJ

Chemical energy store in petrol
100 MJ

Internal energy dissipated in heating up the engine
60 MJ

Sound waves transfer energy to air and surrounding objects
17 MJ

Conservation of Energy

As shown in the above Sankey diagrams, a lot of energy dissipates during transfers. However, there are several ways of reducing unwanted energy transfers.

Lubrication and Aerodynamics

Moving objects have frictional forces acting upon them. These forces transfer a system's energy from its kinetic energy store to its internal/thermal energy store.

Making an object more aerodynamic reduces the air resistance acting upon it and, therefore, the amount of wasted energy. Travelling more slowly also reduces air resistance.

Additionally, objects that rub together create frictional forces that result in wasted internal / thermal energy. Lubricants, such as oil, can be used to reduce friction.

Insulation

The higher the thermal conductivity of a material, the higher the rate of energy transfer by conduction through that material.

Because of this, materials with low thermal conductivity are often used to build thick walls in new houses to reduce heat loss. Walls are also built with an air gap between them to reduce energy loss.

Using thermal insulation reduces the movement of particles from hotter areas to cooler areas by convection currents. Likewise, loft insulation, double-glazed windows and draught excluders reduce heat loss through convection.

daydream
EDUCATION

Thermal insulation helps to keep things warm or cool by reducing unwanted energy transfers in a system. The following investigation explores the effectiveness of different materials as thermal insulators.

Be careful when performing this investigation as it involves using hot water.

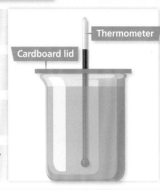

1 Boil water in a kettle, and pour a set volume (e.g. 80 cm³) into a beaker.

Thermometer

Cardboard lid

2 Use a piece of cardboard as a lid for the beaker, and make a hole for a thermometer.

3 Put the thermometer through the lid so that its bulb is in the hot water.

4 Record the temperature of the water as soon as the thermometer has stopped rising and then at 3-minute intervals for 15 minutes.

5 Record your results in a table.

Material	Water Temperature (°C)						Overall Temperature Decrease (°C)
	Start	3 min	6 min	9 min	12 min	15 min	

6 Repeat steps 1–5 but wrap different materials, such as bubble wrap, corrugated cardboard and aluminium foil, around the beaker and lid. Ensure that control variables such as the volume and temperature of the water are the same for each experiment.

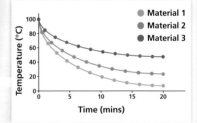

7 Plot a graph like the one to the right to show the cooling curve for each material.

The insulating material that leads to the smallest decrease in temperature is the best thermal insulator.

Extension work: Select one of your test materials and repeat the investigation with a different number of layers of material wrapped around the container.

Efficiency

Efficiency is a measure of the proportion of the total input energy, work or power that is turned into useful output. The less energy dissipated from a system, the more efficient it is.

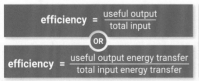

$$\text{efficiency} = \frac{\text{useful output}}{\text{total input}}$$

OR

$$\text{efficiency} = \frac{\text{useful output energy transfer}}{\text{total input energy transfer}}$$

A solar cell can usefully convert 4 J of input energy into 0.6 J of output energy every second.

Therefore, the efficiency of the solar cell is 0.15 or 15%.

$$\text{efficiency} = \frac{\text{useful output}}{\text{total input}}$$
$$= \frac{0.6}{4}$$
$$= 0.15$$

daydream EDUCATION

Energy Resources

Sources of energy, or energy resources, are used for generating electricity and for transport, heating and cooking. Each energy resource has different benefits and drawbacks.

Non-Renewable Resources

These resources are finite and will eventually run out. Once they are depleted, they cannot be replenished.

FOSSIL FUELS

 Coal

 Natural gas

 Crude oil

 Nuclear

Renewable Resources

These resources are infinite. They can be easily replenished and will not run out.

 Solar (Sun)

 Wind

Geothermal

Biofuels

Hydroelectric

Tidal & wave

Changing Demand for Fuel in the UK

Traditionally, the UK's energy mix has consisted mainly of the fossil fuels coal, gas and oil. However, fossil fuel reserves are declining, and efforts are being made to reduce greenhouse gas emissions. As such, a big shift from fossil fuels to renewable energy sources is occurring.

The EU aims to have 32% of its energy mix made up of renewable energy by 2030.

UK Electricity Generation

2009   2020

Gas   Renewables   Nuclear   Coal   Other   Oil

How Different Energy Resources Are Used

Transport

Transport is one of the biggest contributors to greenhouse gas emissions in the UK, with oil-based fuels such as petrol, diesel and kerosene being the most popular fuels for transport.

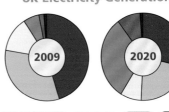

Alternative renewable energy resources include biofuels and electrically-powered vehicles (if recharged using electricity from renewable power stations).

Heating

Most of the energy used in domestic heating comes from natural gas. However, electric heaters and wood, coal and heating oil burners are also used.

Energy consumption from heating can be reduced through improved efficiency – for example improved insulation, underfloor heating and the use of smart meters.

The UK's electricity supply comes from a wide variety of sources, with over 60% being generated from fossil fuels (mainly gas and coal). Nuclear power and renewable energy resources (mainly wind and biomass) make up most of the remaining 40%.

Fossil Fuels

The burning of fossil fuels releases CO_2 into the atmosphere and is the main source of greenhouse gas emissions. It is believed that the increase in greenhouse gases in the atmosphere has contributed to global warming, which has a significant effect on the environment and people.

Warmer global temperatures will cause glaciers and ice sheets to melt, leading to rising sea levels and the loss of polar habitats.

Rising sea levels will result in low-lying coastal areas flooding more frequently or even becoming permanently submerged in water.

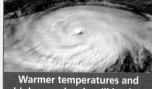

Warmer temperatures and higher sea levels will lead to more extreme weather and a change in precipitation patterns.

Other products of fossil fuel combustion include carbon monoxide, sulfur dioxide, soot and nitrogen oxide. These also affect human health and the environment, causing acid rain, smog and global dimming.

Alternative Energy Resources

To reduce dependence on fossil fuels, governments are looking to increase the use of alternative energy resources that are renewable and cause less damage to the environment.

Renewable energy sources are a good option for increasing the energy supply because they do not run out. However, each source has its associated advantages and disadvantages.

	Use	Advantage	Disadvantage
Biomass 	Organic materials, such as animal waste, wood and crops, are burned for energy or processed into biofuel.	Biomass is affordable and renewable if resources are replaced (e.g. trees are replanted).	Burning biomass releases CO_2. Using wood for fuel can lead to deforestation.
Wind 	The generators in wind turbines use the kinetic energy store in the wind to produce electricity.	Wind power produces no greenhouse gases. Once turbines have been set up, wind is a cheap source of energy.	Set-up costs are high. Some people consider turbines an eyesore, and they also create noise pollution.

daydream
EDUCATION

Hydroelectric Power (HEP) 	Dams are used to trap and control water. As water is released, its kinetic energy store is used to turn turbines which are connected to electric generators.	Once infrastructure has been set up, HEP produces energy cheaply. Reservoirs provide a water supply during shortages.	Set-up costs are high. Also, when dams are built, habitats are often destroyed and people displaced.
Tidal	Currents and changes in tidal water levels are used to turn turbines and produce electricity.	Tides are guaranteed and predictable, and they produce no greenhouse gases.	Tidal barrages are costly to build and can disrupt ecosystems.
Geothermal 	Heat from within the Earth is used to generate electricity.	Geothermal energy is a cheap energy source.	Power can only be harnessed from tectonically active areas.
Wave 	Electricity is generated when waves turn turbines in the sea.	Wave power produces no greenhouse gases. It is well-suited to coastal areas.	It is costly to set up and produces little energy when the sea is calm.
Solar 	Solar panels are used to convert the Sun's energy into electricity.	Once solar panels have been set up, solar energy is cheap. It produces no greenhouse gases.	No electricity is generated when there is no sunlight. Panels are expensive.

In addition to efforts to use more renewable energy resources, existing energy generation can be made more efficient.

Fossil Fuels

Power stations can reuse wasted heat or burn biomass as they generate electricity. New technologies can also be used to exploit resources that were once too difficult to extract – for example, fracking for shale gas.

Nuclear Power

Nuclear power stations can generate a lot of electricity without producing polluting gases. Used uranium rods can also be reused to improve efficiency. However, nuclear waste is highly dangerous, and any accidents from nuclear plants could be disastrous.

Reliability of Energy Resources

Few renewable energy resources are competitive with fossil fuels for cost, energy generation and reliability. However, fossil fuels are non-renewable and will eventually run out. Therefore, countries need to consider investing in alternative methods of energy production to ensure the long-term provision of energy.

Circuit Symbols

Electrical circuit diagrams can sometimes look confusing. Here is an explanation of the most commonly used symbols.

Commonly Used Symbols

Cell

A cell is a store of chemical energy.

Switch

A switch can be turned on (closed) to let current flow or turned off (open) to stop current flow.

Motor

A motor turns current into motion, for example, in a hair dryer.

Resistor

A fixed resistor controls the amount of current in a circuit.

Voltmeter

A voltmeter is used to measure the potential difference between two points in an electrical circuit.

Fuse

A fuse helps protect electrical circuits. It is usually a thin wire that melts and causes the circuit to break if too large a current flows through it.

LDR

A light-dependent resistor (LDR) adapts to the amount of light it receives. As light intensity increases, resistance decreases.

daydream
EDUCATIO

Battery

A battery is two or more cells connected in series.

Diode

A diode allows current to flow in one direction only. It is normally used to prevent damage to other components.

LED

A light-emitting diode (LED) emits light when current flows the correct way through it.

Variable Resistor

A variable resistor can be adjusted to control the amount of current in a circuit.

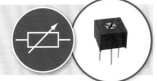

Ammeter

An ammeter is used to measure current.

Bulb/Lamp

A bulb or lamp lights up only when it is in a circuit that is complete.

Thermistor

A thermistor is a type of resistor. Its resistance varies significantly with temperature.

Electrical Current, Potential Difference & Resistance

Electrical Charge and Current

Current is the flow of electrical charge. It is measured in amperes **(A)**, or amps, using an ammeter. The measurement is the same at any point in a single closed-circuit loop. The size of the current is the rate of flow of electrical charge.

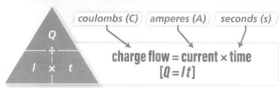

coulombs (C) amperes (A) seconds (s)

charge flow = current × time
$$[Q = It]$$

The charge that passes a point in a circuit is 1 coulomb when there is a current of 1 amp for 1 second.

Example

The current in a series circuit is 3.0 A. How much charge flows though the circuit in 5 minutes?

$Q = It$
$Q = 3.0 \times (5 \times 60)$
$Q = 3.0 \times 300$
$Q = 900\ C$

Current, Potential Difference and Resistance

Potential Difference

For an electrical charge to flow through a closed circuit, there must be a potential difference to 'push' the charge around. Potential difference is measured in volts (V) using a voltmeter.

For a fixed resistance, the bigger the potential difference, the greater the current.

Resistance

Some components require a large potential difference to produce a current through them. This is because they have a high resistance (opposition to the flow of electrical charge). Resistance is measured in ohms (Ω).

For a fixed potential difference, the greater the resistance of a component, the smaller the current.

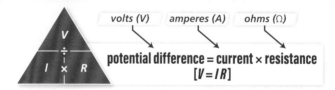

volts (V) amperes (A) ohms (Ω)

potential difference = current × resistance
$$[V = IR]$$

Example

The potential difference across the lamp is 9 V, and the current is 0.3 A.

Calculate the resistance of the lamp in this circuit.

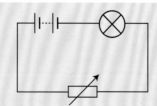

$R = \dfrac{V}{I}$

$R = \dfrac{9}{0.3}$

$R = 30\ \Omega$

Photocopying or scanning this image is a breach of copyright law.

daydream

There are various factors that affect the resistance of electrical circuits. The following practical activity can be used to determine how the length of a wire at a constant temperature affects the resistance.

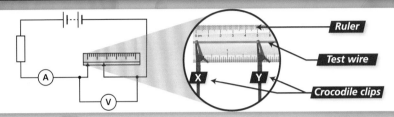

Ruler

Test wire

Crocodile clips

1 Set up the circuit as shown so you can measure the potential difference across and current through a test wire at different lengths. The voltmeter must be in parallel across the test wire.

2 Using a crocodile clip (X), connect the lead from the negative side of the ammeter to the test wire at zero on the ruler.

3 The lead from the negative side of the battery is then connected to the test wire at set intervals (e.g. every 5 cm) using another crocodile clip (Y). This lead is used as a switch for the battery between readings.

4 Create a table like the one below to record the results.

Length of wire (cm)	Potential Difference (V)	Current (A)	Resistance (Ω)
5			
10			
...			

5 Connect crocodile clip Y at the first distance, and measure the readings on the voltmeter and ammeter. Record the measurements in the table.

6 Disconnect crocodile clip Y and repeat step 5 for all intervals - 10 cm, 15 cm and so on.

7 Calculate the resistance for each length of wire using the following equation:

$$\text{resistance } (\Omega) = \frac{\text{potential difference (V)}}{\text{current (A)}}$$

8 Plot a graph of resistance against wire length. The resistance of the wire is directly proportional to its length so the graph should be a straight line through the origin.

There is a good chance that your graph may not pass through the origin. It is difficult to measure the length of the wire at 0 cm accurately, and there will be some contact resistance between the wire and the crocodile clips.

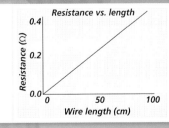

17

Resistance

The current through a component in a circuit is not always proportional to the potential difference across it. The resistance may change as the current changes.

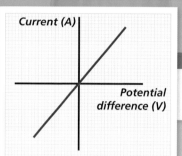

Ohmic Conductor (at a Constant Temperature)

The current through an ohmic conductor is directly proportional to the potential difference across it. Resistance remains constant as the current changes.

Filament Lamp

Resistance increases with temperature. Therefore, as current passes through the filament, the filament heats up, and resistance increases.

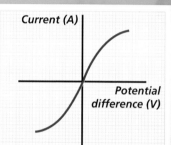

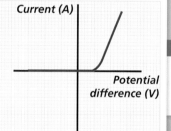

Diode

The current through a diode flows in one direction only. The diode has a very high resistance in the reverse direction and a very low resistance in the forward direction.

The resistance of some components changes in response to a change in their environment.

Thermistors

The resistance of a thermistor decreases as the temperature increases and vice versa. As a result, they are used in many applications such as fire alarms, air-conditioning units and fridges as a thermostat (temperature sensor).

LDRs

The resistance of an LDR decreases as light intensity increases and vice versa. As a result, they are used in many applications that require lights to be switched on when it gets dark, such as night lights and outdoor lighting.

The following practical activity can be used to investigate the
I-V characteristics of resistors, filament lamps and diodes.

1 Set up the circuit as shown opposite.

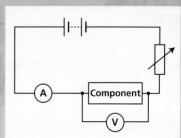

2 Connect a resistor to the circuit (where it says component)
and set the variable resistor to a suitable value.

3 Record the readings on the ammeter and voltmeter in
a suitable table.

4 Adjust the variable resistor to a new value, and record the new readings.

5 Repeat step 4, changing the resistance of the variable resistor, to obtain several pairs of readings.

6 Swap the connections on the battery so the direction of current is reversed, and record the
readings on the ammeter and voltmeter. The readings should now be negative.

7 As before, adjust the variable resistor several times, and record the pairs of readings of
current and potential difference.

8 Plot a graph of current against potential difference. It should look like the ohmic conductor
graph in the Resistance section.

9 Replace the resistor with a filament lamp and repeat steps 1–8. The resulting graph should
look like the filament lamp graph in the Resistance section.

10 To investigate the I-V characteristics of a diode,
you will need to set up the circuit slightly differently,
as shown opposite.

Reduce the battery pd to less than 5 V, connect an
extra resistor (P) and replace the ammeter with
a milliammeter (mA).

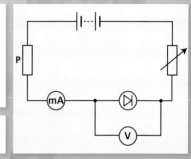

11 Repeat step 3–8. The resulting graph should look
like the diode graph in the Resistance section.

Series & Parallel Circuits

Parallel Circuit

In a parallel circuit, components are placed on separate branches and each branch can be switched on and off independently. Also, if a component in one branch fails, the components in other branches will continue to work.

Series Circuit

In a series circuit, all components are connected in a single closed-circuit loop. Therefore, if one component breaks, all other components will fail.

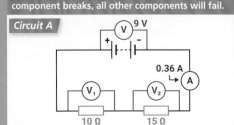

Circuit A

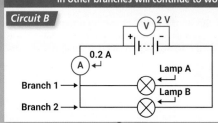

Circuit B

The current (*I*) through each of the components is the same: $I_1 = I_2 = I_3$ ...
The current through all components in circuit A is 0.36 A.

current = potential difference ÷ resistance
= 9 ÷ (10 + 15)
= 9 ÷ 25
= 0.36 A

Current

The total current through a circuit is the sum of the current through each branch. The current splits between each branch and then recombines.

If two components of the same resistance are connected in parallel, the same current will flow through them. For example, the current through lamps A and B is 0.1 A.

The total potential difference (voltage) of the power supply is shared between the components according to their resistance.

potential difference = current × resistance	
$V_1 = 0.36 × 10$	$V_2 = 0.36 × 15$
= 3.6 V	= 5.4 V

Potential Difference

The potential difference across each branch is the same. In circuit B, the potential difference across both lamps is 2 V.

If an additional lamp were added to branch 2, in series with lamp B, the potential difference of 2 V would be shared between the two lamps, and 1 V would go to each.

The total resistance of two components in a series circuit, is the sum of their resistances:
$R_{total} = R_1 + R_2 + R_3$ ...

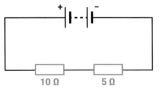

Resistance

The current in a parallel circuit can take multiple paths. Therefore, the resistance of the whole circuit is less than the resistance of any of the individual resistors.

$$\frac{1}{R_{total}} = \frac{1}{R_1} + \frac{1}{R_2} ...$$

The total resistance	$R_{total} = R_1 + R_2$
in the circuit	= 10 + 5
is 15 Ω.	= 15 Ω

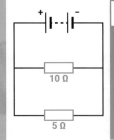

The total resistance in the circuit is **3.3 Ω**.

$$\frac{1}{R_{total}} = \frac{1}{10} + \frac{1}{5}$$

$$\frac{1}{R_{total}} = 0.1 + 0.2$$

$$\frac{1}{R_{total}} = 0.3$$

$$R_{total} = \frac{1}{0.3}$$

$$= 3.3 Ω$$

daydream EDUCATION

Electric current can only flow if there is a complete circuit. There are two ways of joining electrical components: in series and in parallel. Some circuits include both series and parallel parts.

Investigating Resistance in Series and Parallel Circuits

The following investigation can be used to determine how the arrangement of resistors in series and in parallel affects resistance.

1 Set up the series circuit as shown opposite. The meters should be positioned as shown.

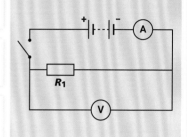

2 Switch on the circuit and record the voltage, or potential difference, across the resistor and the current through it.

3 Calculate the value of the resistor R_1:

resistance = $\dfrac{\text{potential difference}}{\text{current}}$ or $R = \dfrac{V}{I}$

4 Take out resistor R_1, replace it with a different resistor (R_2), and repeat steps 2–3 to ensure R_1 and R_2 have the same value of resistance.

5 Set up the series circuit as shown opposite. Use wire wound resistors because they are less likely to overheat (and cause anomalous results).

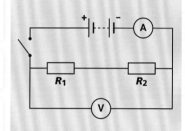

6 Switch on the circuit, and record the readings of the ammeter and the voltmeter.

7 Calculate the total resistance of the circuit: $R = \dfrac{V}{I}$

8 Set up the parallel circuit as shown, using the same resistors (R_1 and R_2) that were used in the series circuit.

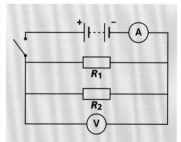

9 Switch on the circuit, and record the readings of the ammeter and the voltmeter.

10 Calculate the total resistance of the circuit: $R = \dfrac{V}{I}$

By performing this investigation, you should be able to reach the following conclusions:

As more resistors are added in series, the total resistance of the circuit will increase. The total resistance of the two resistors R_1 and R_2 is $R_1 + R_2$.

Conversely, as more resistors are added in parallel, the total resistance of the circuit will decrease. The total resistance of two resistors in parallel is less than the resistance of each individual resistor.

Electricity in the Home

Direct and Alternating Potential Difference

Electrical supplies can be direct current (dc) or alternating current (ac).

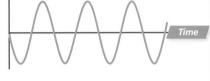

Direct Current (dc)

Potential Difference (V)

Time

In a direct current (dc) circuit, the battery or power supply provides a direct potential difference. This causes current to flow in one direction only, from the + to the – of the battery or power supply.

Alternating Current (ac)

Potential Difference (V)

Time

In an alternating power supply, the potential difference is constantly changing direction. This causes the current to go one way around the circuit and then the other, repeatedly.

Mains electricity is an alternating (ac) supply. In the UK, the domestic electricity supply has a frequency of 50 Hz and is about 230 V. The current alternates (goes one way then the other) 50 times per second.

Mains Electricity

In the home, most electrical appliances are connected to the mains supply by a three-pin plug at the end of a three-core cable.

The insulation around each wire is colour coded.

Live Wire (Brown)

The brown live wire carries the alternating potential difference from the plug socket to the appliance.

Neutral Wire (Blue)

The blue neutral wire completes the circuit. The live and neutral wires carry current to and from the appliance.

Earth Wire (Green and Yellow Stripes)

The green-and-yellow striped earth wire is a safety wire. There is a current in this wire only when the appliance circuit has developed a fault.

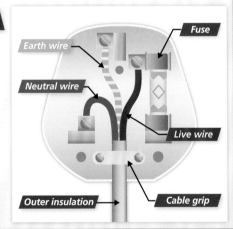

Earth wire
Fuse
Neutral wire
Live wire
Outer insulation
Cable grip

The earth wire is at a potential of 0 V. The potential difference between the live and earth wires is about 230 V. The neutral wire is very close to earth potential (0 V). The live wire can be dangerous even when the circuit is switched off. The fuse in the three pin plug helps reduce this danger by creating a gap (break) in the live part of the circuit when it fuses, melts or blows.

daydream EDUCATION

Energy Transfers in Electrical Appliances

Energy Transfer

Everyday electrical appliances transfer chemical energy from batteries or ac mains to other energy stores by electricity. Work is done to move a charge round the circuit.

In an electric motor, energy is transferred from the chemical energy store in the battery to the kinetic energy store in the motor.

In a kettle, energy is transferred from the energy store in the ac mains to the thermal energy store of the heating element in the kettle.

| **Battery** Chemical energy store | → *Electric current* → | **Motor** Kinetic energy store | **ac mains** Energy store | → *Electric current* → | **Kettle** Thermal energy store |

Remember that not all energy is transferred usefully – some is dissipated, or wasted.

The amount of energy transferred by an appliance depends on how long the appliance has been switched on and the power of the appliance.

$$\frac{E}{P \times t}$$

joules (J)　watts (W)　seconds (s)

energy transferred = power × time

$$[E = Pt]$$

A kettle has a power rating of 2.2 kW and takes 2 minutes and 30 seconds to boil the water inside it. Calculate the energy transferred to the water.

$E = Pt$
$= 2,200 \times (2.5 \times 60)$
$= 330,000 \text{ J or } 330 \text{ kJ}$

The energy transferred can also be calculated using the following equation:

$$\frac{E}{V \times Q}$$

joules (J)　volts (V)　coulombs (C)

energy transferred = potential difference × charge

$$[E = VQ]$$

The amount of charge in a circuit depends on the size of the current and how long it has been switched on for. Therefore, charge can be calculated using the following equation:

$$\frac{Q}{I \times t}$$

coulombs (C)　amperes (A)　seconds (s)

charge = current × time

$$[Q = It]$$

A 12 V battery supplies a 3.2 A current through a motor for 14 minutes.
How much energy is transferred from the battery to the motor?

1 First calculate the charge.

$$Q = It$$
$$= 3.2 \times (14 \times 60)$$
$$= 2,688 \, C$$

2 Now calculate the energy transferred.

$$E = VQ$$
$$= 2,688 \times 12$$
$$= 32,300 \, J \, (3 \, s.f.)$$

Power

The power transferred in any electrical circuit depends on the potential difference across it and the current through it.

$$\frac{P}{V \times I}$$

watts (W)   volts (V)   amps (A)

power = potential difference × current
$$[P = VI]$$

How big is the current in a 2 kW electric kettle connected to the UK (230 V) mains supply?

$$current = \frac{power}{potential\ difference}$$
$$= \frac{2,000}{230}$$
$$= 8.7 \, A \, (2 \, s.f.)$$

Because potential difference = current × resistance, the equation can also be represented as follows:

power = current² × resistance
$$[P = I^2R]$$

When connected to the UK (230 V) mains supply, the resistance of a 100 W filament lamp is measured as 529 Ω. Calculate the current in the lamp filament.

1 First, rearrange the equation to make current the subject.

$$I^2 = \frac{P}{R}$$

2 Now calculate the current in the lamp filament.

$$I^2 = \frac{100}{529}$$
$$I^2 = 0.189$$
$$I = \sqrt{0.189}$$
$$= 0.435 \, A \, (3 \, s.f.)$$

Power Ratings for Electrical Appliances

Domestic electrical appliances often have a power rating label that displays information such as the power of the appliance (how much electrical energy it transfers in a second) and the potential difference of the supply. From this, it is possible to calculate the current.

An iron with a power rating of 1200 W is connected to the 230 V mains supply. Calculate the current the iron draws from the mains supply.

$$I = \frac{P}{V}$$
$$I = \frac{1,200}{230}$$
$$= 5.2 \, A \, (2 \, s.f.)$$

daydream EDUCATION

The National Grid

Electrical power is generated by power stations. This is then transferred across the country through the National Grid.

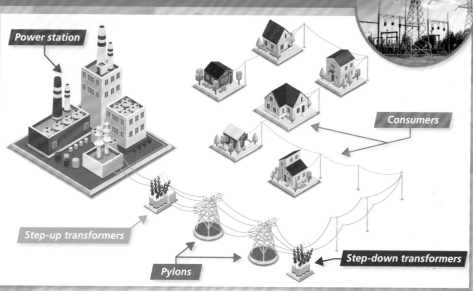

Power station

Consumers

Step-up transformers

Pylons

Step-down transformers

Step-up transformers are used to increase the potential difference from the power station to the cables that form the network across the UK.

Step-down transformers are used to decrease the potential difference to a much lower value (230 V) for use in our homes.

A step-up transformer increases the potential difference but reduces the current in the cables of the National Grid. This reduces the energy dissipated (or lost) through heating of the cables.

The potential difference can be as large as 400,000 V (400 kV), which is very dangerous, so pylons are used to keep the cables a safe distance away from people.

daydream
EDUCATION

Static Electricity

Current electricity is a flow of electrical charge. Static electricity is when charges are not free to move, usually on an insulator. This causes a build-up of electric charge.

An electrical charge can build up through frictional contact between two insulators. A conductor would let the stationary charges move.

Static electricity is caused by an imbalance of negative and positive charges on an object. When certain insulating materials are rubbed against each other, they become electrically charged. Negatively charged electrons rub off one material and on to the other.

The material that gains electrons has a net negative charge and is negatively charged. The material that loses electrons has an equal net positive charge and is positively charged. Electrons remain, but there are now more positive charges than negative charges. Positive charges do not move.

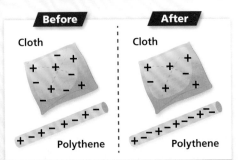

When a cloth is rubbed against a polythene rod, negatively charged electrons rub off the cloth and on to the polythene rod.

The polythene becomes negatively charged, and the cloth becomes positively charged.

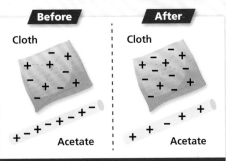

When a cloth is rubbed against an acetate rod, negatively charged electrons rub off the acetate and on to the cloth.

The acetate becomes positively charged, and the cloth becomes negatively charged.

When two electrically charged objects are brought close together, they exert a force on each other.

Two objects that carry the same type of charge repel.

Two objects that carry different types of charge attract.

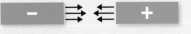

Attraction and repulsion between two charged objects are examples of **non-contact forces**.

daydream
EDUCATION

Electric Charges and Fields

A charged object creates a radial electric field that radiates from its surface. The field gets weaker as the distance from the object increases.

Radial field

When a second charged object is placed in the field, it experiences a force. The closer this object is to the original object, the stronger the force it experiences.

The type of charges determines how the objects interact with each other. Two objects with the same electric charge repel, and two objects with opposite electric charges attract.

If the original object has a net positive charge, the arrows point outward, and the second (positively charged) object is repelled away from the original object.

If the original object has a net negative charge, the arrows point inward, and the second (positively charged) object is attracted towards the original object.

Sparks and Electric Shocks

Static charge builds up on an object until it can be released or discharged.

Electrons

For example, when you walk across a carpet, the friction between your shoes and the carpet causes a transfer of electrons from the carpet to your body, so your body becomes negatively charged.

The charge remains until it can be released, such as when you touch a conductor (e.g. a metal door handle). The extra electrons jump from you to the handle, causing a shock.

The greater the charge produced on an object, the stronger the electric field becomes and the greater the shock.

Lightning is a powerful example of static electricity. Convection currents in the air make ice crystals in a thunder cloud rub together. The bottom of the cloud then becomes negatively charged and an electrostatic energy store.

The potential difference between the charged cloud and Earth can be several million volts. Therefore, when the electric charge is released, it is huge.

When the cloud discharges, electrical work is done as the charge flows from the cloud down to Earth. Energy is transferred to the surroundings mainly by heat caused by the spark, as well as by sound (thunder) and radiation (lightning).

States of Matter

The three states of matter are solid, liquid and gas. In chemical equations, the three states of matter are shown as (s), (l) and (g), with (aq) for aqueous solutions.

States of Matter

Particle theory is a basic model that helps to explain the properties and behaviour of materials in each of the three states. It enables us to visualise what is happening on a very small scale.

Solid

Particle Arrangement & Behaviour
- Strong forces of attraction between particles
- Usually in a regular arrangement
- Particles are close together and vibrate about fixed positions

Properties
- Has a definite shape
- Has a definite volume
- Usually has a high density
- Cannot easily be compressed. The atoms are closely packed together, so there is a lot of mass in a small volume.

Liquid

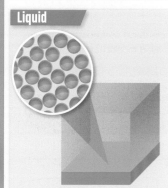

Particle Arrangement & Behaviour
- Weak forces of attraction between particles
- Random arrangement
- Particles move about freely but are close together

Properties
- Takes the shape of its container
- Has a definite volume
- Cannot easily be compressed. The atoms are closely packed together, so there is a lot of mass in a small volume.

Gas

Particle Arrangement & Behaviour
- Very weak forces of attraction between particles
- Random arrangement
- Particles move around freely at high speed and are far apart

Properties
- Takes the shape of its container
- Does not have a definite shape or volume
- Can easily be compressed. The atoms are not closely packed together, so there are few atoms in a given volume.

daydream
EDUCATI

Although particle theory can explain the different states of matter and the differences in density of substances, it has some limitations as a model. For example, particles are not solid spheres, and the forces between the particles are not represented in the model.

State Changes – *Most substances can exist in all three states.*

During a change in state, mass is never lost or gained: it is conserved.

The amount of energy needed to change state – from solid to liquid and from liquid to gas – depends on the strength of the forces between particles in a substance. The stronger the forces, the higher the melting point and boiling point of the substance.

State changes are physical changes that can be reversed. The chemical composition of the particles remains the same, but their arrangement, movement and amount of energy change.

 Boiling and evaporation are both changes of state from liquid to gas. Evaporation takes place at any temperature, but boiling occurs only at the boiling point.

| Solid | Melting: when a solid changes into a liquid | Liquid | Boiling/Evaporation: when a liquid changes into a gas | Gas |

Heat in →
← **Heat out**

Heat in →
← **Heat out**

| **Ice** (10 grams) | Freezing: when a liquid changes into a solid | **Water** (10 grams) | Condensation: when a gas changes into a liquid | **Steam** (10 grams) |

A substance can also change state from a solid to a gas without passing through a liquid phase. This is known as sublimation. For example, dry ice (solid CO_2) sublimates from a solid to a gas at room temperature.

Density of Materials

The density of a substance indicates how compact it is. It is measured by mass per unit volume.

The density of a material can be calculated using the following equation:

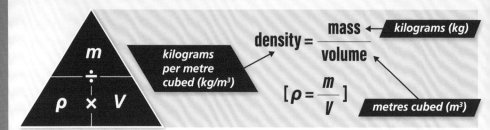

$$density = \frac{mass}{volume}$$

kilograms (kg)

metres cubed (m³)

$$[\rho = \frac{m}{V}]$$

m ÷ ρ × V

kilograms per metre cubed (kg/m³)

Solids and liquids are usually denser than gases. Their atoms are closely packed together, so there is a lot of mass in a small volume. In gases, the atoms or molecules are much further apart, so there is less mass in the same volume.

A balloon contains helium with a mass of 0.00254 kg. The balloon has a volume of 0.0141 m³. Calculate the density of helium.

$$density = \frac{mass}{volume}$$

$$= \frac{0.00254}{0.0141}$$

$$= 0.18 \text{ (2 s.f.)}$$

The density of helium is 0.18 kg/m³.

Copper has a density of 8,900 kg/m³. Calculate the volume of 500 g of copper.

$$volume = \frac{mass}{density}$$

$$= \frac{0.5}{8900}$$

$$= 0.000056 \text{ (2 s.f.)}$$

The volume of 500 g of copper is 0.000056 m³ or 5.6 × 10⁻⁵ m³.

daydrea
EDUCATE

Practical Activity:
The density of regular and irregular solid objects and liquids can be determined using the following methods.

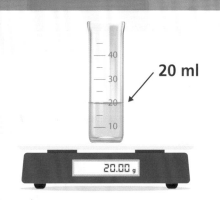

20 ml

Liquids

1. Place a measuring cylinder on a balance, and set the scale to zero.
2. Pour 20 ml of the liquid into a cylinder, and record the mass.
3. Add another 20 ml of the liquid, and record the new mass and volume.
4. Repeat this process, and then calculate the density of the substance for each set of measurements (1 ml = 1 cm³).
5. Calculate an average density from the results.

Regular Solid Objects

1. Measure the length, width and height of the object.
2. Calculate the volume of the object with the appropriate formula.
3. Measure the mass of the object with a balance.
4. Calculate the density using the mass and volume.

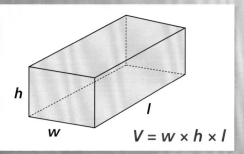

h
l
w
$V = w \times h \times l$

Irregular Non-Porous Solid Objects

1. Measure the mass of the object with a balance.
2. Pour some water into a measuring cylinder (there needs to be enough water to submerge the object) and record the volume.
3. Place the object into the cylinder, and record the new volume.
4. The difference in volume between the first and second measurement is the volume of the object.
5. Use the mass and volume to calculate the density of the object.

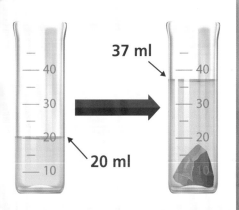

37 ml

20 ml

Internal Energy & Energy Transfers

Energy is stored inside a system by the particles (atoms and molecules) that make up the system. Internal energy is the total kinetic energy and potential energy of all the particles (atoms and molecules) that make up the system.

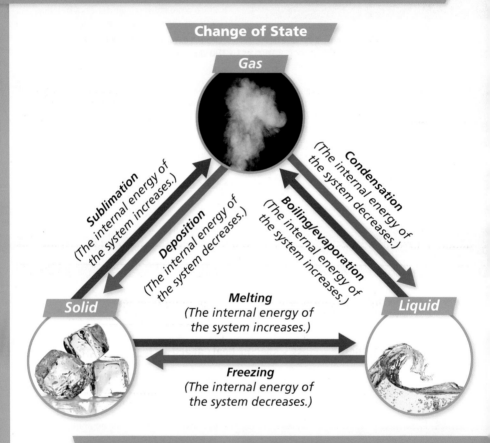

Change of State

Gas

Sublimation
(The internal energy of the system increases.)

Deposition
(The internal energy of the system decreases.)

Condensation
(The internal energy of the system decreases.)

Boiling/evaporation
(The internal energy of the system increases.)

Solid

Melting
(The internal energy of the system increases.)

Freezing
(The internal energy of the system decreases.)

Liquid

Heating a system increases the energy of its particles, which leads to a change in either temperature or state. A change in state occurs if the particles in the system have enough energy to break their bonds.

Key Point

Temperature (°C) is a measure of how hot something is, whereas heat (J) is a measure of the thermal energy contained within an object.

daydrea
EDUCAT

Temperature Changes and Specific Heat Capacity

When the temperature of a system is increased by supplying energy to its thermal energy store, the resulting increase in temperature depends upon:

- The mass of the substance
- The type of material (what it is made of)
- The energy put into the system

Therefore, different amounts of energy are needed to increase the temperature of different substances by the same level.

It takes 130 J to increase the temperature of 1 kg of lead by 1°C, whereas it takes 4,200 J to increase the temperature of 1 kg of water by 1°C. Because of water's high specific heat capacity, it is used a lot in temperature regulation.

Specific Heat Capacity
The amount of energy needed to change the temperature of 1 kg of a substance by 1°C

The amount of energy stored in or released from a system as its temperature changes can be calculated by using the equation:

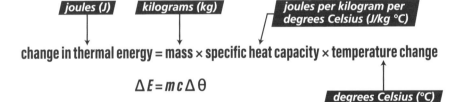

joules (J) kilograms (kg) joules per kilogram per degrees Celsius (J/kg °C)

change in thermal energy = mass × specific heat capacity × temperature change

$$\Delta E = m c \Delta \theta$$

degrees Celsius (°C)

Example

How much heat energy is needed to heat 5 kg of water from 15°C to 68°C, given that the specific heat capacity of water is 4,200 J/kg°C?

$$\Delta E = m c \Delta \theta$$

$$= 5 \times 4,200 \times (68 - 15)$$

$$= 1,113,000 \text{ J or } 1,113 \text{ kJ or } 1.11 \text{ MJ}$$

The following investigation is used to measure the specific heat capacity of different metals. The specific heat capacity is determined by linking the decrease of one energy store (or work done) to the increase in temperature of the material.

1 Measure the mass of the metal block. The block must have two holes: one for the immersion heater and one for the thermometer.

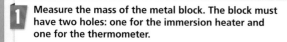

2 Wrap the metal in an insulating material.

3 Place the thermometer and immersion heater into the holes.

4 Record the temperature of the metal block.

5 Connect the heater to the power supply, set the power pack to 12 V and switch it on.

6 Record the ammeter and voltmeter readings, which should not change. Then calculate the power of the heater in watts:

power = potential difference × current

7 Record the temperature of the metal block every minute for 10 minutes, and then switch off the power supply. Use a table like the one below to record the results.

Time (s)	Temperature (°C)	Power of Heater (W)	Work Done (J)

8 Calculate the energy transferred (work done) by the heater: work done = time × power. Record the results in your table.

9 Plot a graph of the temperature against work done and draw a line of best fit.

10 Calculate the gradient of the straight line:

$$\text{gradient} = \frac{\text{change in temperature}}{\text{change in work done}}$$

11 Calculate the heat capacity of the block of metal:

$$\text{heat capacity} = \frac{1}{\text{gradient}}$$

12 Calculate the specific heat capacity of the block of metal:

$$\text{specific heat capacity} = \frac{\text{heat capacity of block}}{\text{mass of block}}$$

Your value for specific heat capacity is likely to be higher than the accepted value. Why do you think this is?

daydream
EDUCATI

Specific Latent Heat

When a substance changes state, a change in energy is required. This energy is called latent heat.

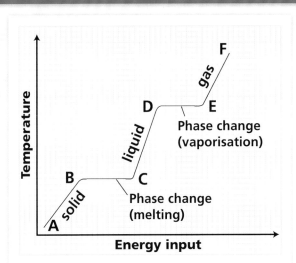

When a substance melts or boils, its internal energy increases. However, the energy is not used to increase its temperature; it is used to overcome the forces of attraction between the particles to enable a change in state.

When a substance condenses or freezes, its internal energy decreases and energy is released. Its temperature does not decrease until the change in state is complete.

Specific Latent Heat

The amount of energy required to change the state of 1 kg of a substance without a change in the temperature

joules (J) *kilograms (kg)* *joules per kilogram (J/kg)*

energy for change of state = mass × specific latent heat

$$E = mL$$

Specific Latent Heat of Vaporisation

The amount of energy required to convert 1 kg of a substance from liquid to vapour

Example: The specific latent heat of vaporisation for water is 2,257 kJ/kg. How much energy does it take to evaporate 2 kg of water at 100°C?

$E = mL$

$= 2 \times 2,257,000$

$= 4,514,000$ J or 4,514 kJ

Specific Latent Heat of Fusion

The amount of energy required to convert 1 kg of a substance from solid to liquid

Example: The specific latent heat of fusion for ice is 334 kJ/kg. How much energy does it take to melt 10 g of ice?

$E = mL$

$= 0.01 \times 334,000$

$= 3,340$ J or 3.34 kJ

Particle Model & Pressure

Particle Motion in a Gas

If a gas is kept at a constant volume, changing its temperature causes its pressure to change. Heating increases the pressure, whereas cooling decreases the pressure.

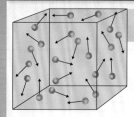

We use the particle model to help us understand, explain and predict the properties of gases.

- The atoms or molecules (particles) in a gas are in constant random motion.
- These particles collide with each other and with the walls of their container without losing any kinetic energy.
- The temperature of the gas is related to the mean kinetic energy in its particles.

When the temperature of the gas increases, so does the mean kinetic energy of the particles. Energy is transferred into the kinetic energy stores of its particles. They move faster, colliding with the walls of their container more frequently and with a greater force. Thus, the pressure increases.

Pressure in a Gas

The atoms in a gas are not closely packed together. Therefore, there are few atoms in a given volume. Because a gas does not have a definite shape or volume, it takes the shape of its container and can easily be compressed.

The pressure of a gas produces a net force at right angles to the wall of the gas container (or any surface). For a fixed mass of gas at a constant temperature:

pascals (Pa) $\longrightarrow$ pressure × volume = constant

metres cubed (m³) $\longrightarrow$ [p V = constant]

Increasing the volume of the container in which a gas is contained, at constant temperature, can lead to a **decrease in pressure**.

The particles have more space to move around so they collide with the walls of the container less frequently. Thus, the pressure decreases.

Conversely, decreasing the volume of the container leads to an **increase in pressure**.

With less space, the individual particles collide with the walls of the container with the same mean force as before but hit the walls more frequently. Thus, the pressure increases.

daydream
EDUCATION

In a container with a volume of 8.0×10^{-3} m³, a gas exerts a pressure of 1.5×10^5 Pa.

Calculate the pressure now exerted by the gas.

The top of the container is sealed by a moveable piston.

The piston is pushed inwards slowly to reduce the volume to 1.0×10^{-3} m³, while the temperature of the gas remains unchanged.

$$p_1 \times V_1 = p_2 \times V_2$$

$$(1.5 \times 10^5) \times (8.0 \times 10^{-3}) = p_2 \times (1.0 \times 10^{-3})$$

$$p_2 = \frac{12 \times 10^2}{1.0 \times 10^{-3}}$$

$$p_2 = 1.2 \times 10^6 \text{ Pa}$$

$V = 8.0 \times 10^{-3}$ m³
$p = 1.5 \times 10^5$ Pa

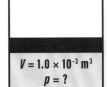

$V = 1.0 \times 10^{-3}$ m³
$p = ?$

Increasing the Pressure of a Gas

Work done is the transfer of energy by a force. Doing mechanical work, specifically, by compressing a gas transfers energy from a chemical energy store to the internal energy store of the gas.

As the internal energy store of the gas increases, its temperature also increases.

For example, when you use a pump to inflate a bike tyre, the end of the pump often gets hot.

This is because a mechanical force is applied to the pump to compress the gas, transferring chemical energy from the muscles to the kinetic energy stores of the gas particles.

Due to the increase in the particles' mean kinetic energy, the extra internal energy of the gas causes an increase in temperature.

The Atom

All substances are made of atoms.
An atom is the smallest part of
an element that can exist.

Development of Atomic Theory

The model of the atom has changed over time as new experimental evidence has been discovered.

| 1803 | 1897 | 1909 | 1913 |

Dalton's Model

Atoms were believed to be tiny spheres that could not be divided.

Thomson's Model

After the discovery of electrons, it was proposed that atoms were balls of positive charge with embedded negative electrons. This model is known as the plum pudding model.

Rutherford's Model

Alpha particle scattering experiments found that the mass of the atom was concentrated at its centre in a positively charged nucleus.

Bohr's Model

Experimental observations showed that electrons move around the nucleus in orbits that are a fixed distance from the nucleus.

In **Rutherford's** experiments, alpha particles were fired at a thin piece of gold foil. Rather than pass through the foil as expected, some particles were deflected, and some bounced back.

This meant that the plum pudding model could not be correct, so Rutherford proposed that there must be a positively charged nucleus at the centre of the atom. This model is known as the nuclear model.

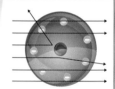

After Bohr's theory of atomic structure was accepted, further experiments by Rutherford showed evidence of smaller positively charged particles (protons) within the nucleus.

This was then developed further, in 1932, with James Chadwick providing evidence to show the existence of neutral particles (neutrons) within the nucleus.

Atoms have no overall electrical charge because they contain an equal number of protons and electrons. Almost all (99.9%) of an atom's mass is in the nucleus.

Atoms turn into positive ions when they lose 1 or more electrons from their outer shell.

Atoms are very small, with a radius of about 0.1 nm (1×10^{-10} m). The radius of a nucleus is less than 1/10,000 of that of the atom (about 1×10^{-14} m).

Particle Name	Relative Charge	Mass
Proton	+1	1
Neutron	0	1
Electron	−1	Very small

daydream EDUCATION

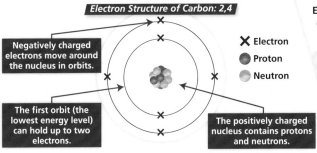

Electron Structure of Carbon: 2,4

Negatively charged electrons move around the nucleus in orbits.

The first orbit (the lowest energy level) can hold up to two electrons.

The positively charged nucleus contains protons and neutrons.

The second and third shells can hold up to eight electrons.

✖ Electron
● Proton
○ Neutron

Electrons are arranged in orbits at different distances (and different energy levels) from the nucleus.

If an electron absorbs electromagnetic (em) radiation it may move further from the nucleus to a higher energy level.

If it moves back closer to the nucleus and a lower energy level, it will emit em radiation.

If an atom were blown up to the size of a football stadium, the nucleus would be the size of a small pea on the centre circle. The electrons would be orbiting around the outermost edge, but they would be far too small to be seen.

Atoms and Elements

The number of protons, electrons and neutrons in atoms varies. However, it is the number of protons in the nucleus of an atom that determines what type of atom it is:

Atom	Number of Protons
Helium	2
Oxygen	8
Aluminium	13

All atoms of a particular element have the same number of protons.

An element is a substance that contains only one type of atom and therefore cannot be broken down into simpler components by any non-nuclear chemical reaction.

Atomic Number & Mass Number

Mass Number
The sum of protons and neutrons in an atom

Atomic Number
This is the number of protons (and electrons) in an atom.

12
C
Carbon
6

Element Symbol
Elements have a one or two-letter chemical symbol. For example, C is the chemical symbol for carbon.

Isotopes

Although atoms of an element will always have the same number of protons (and atomic number), they can have a different number of neutrons and, therefore, a different mass number. These are called isotopes.

12
C
Carbon
6

13
C
Carbon
6

14
C
Carbon
6

Radioactive Decay

The nucleus of a radioactive substance is unstable. To become more stable, the nucleus decays and emits radiation.

Isotopes are forms of an element that have the same number of protons but different numbers of neutrons.

The nuclei of some isotopes (radioactive isotopes) are unstable, so they split up or decay, emitting radiation. When a radioactive isotope decays, it can form a different atom with a different number of protons.

Mass number – The total number of protons and neutrons in an atom

Atomic number – The number of protons in an atom

14
N
Nitrogen
7

Radiation

When a radioactive substance decays, it emits different types of ionising radiation, including:

Radiation	Alpha (α)	Beta (β)	Gamma (γ)
Symbol	$^4_2\alpha$ or ^4_2He	$^0_{-1}\beta$ or $^0_{-1}e$	$^0_0\gamma$
Formation	Two protons and two neutrons are emitted from the nucleus. It is the same as a helium nucleus.	A high-speed electron is ejected from the nucleus as a neutron turns into a proton.	Electromagnetic radiation is emitted from the nucleus.
Penetration	Stopped easily; unable to penetrate skin or paper	Stopped relatively easily; unable to penetrate aluminium (>3 mm thick)	Difficult to stop; unable to penetrate lead (>several centimetres thick)*
Range in Air	A few centimetres	A few metres	A few kilometres
Ionising Power	Very strong due to their size and charge	Moderate	Weak

*Gamma rays have varying amounts of energy because they have different wavelengths and thus different penetrating powers.

daydream
EDUCATION

Activity, measured in becquerel (Bq), is the rate at which unstable nuclei decay. Count-rate is the number of decays recorded each second by a detector, such as a Geiger–Müller tube.

Nuclear Fission

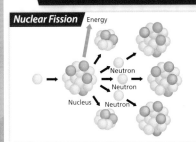
Energy
Neutron
Neutron
Nucleus
Neutron

Neutrons are emitted from some very unstable nuclei. The neutrons are a dangerous form of radiation.

Neutron emission is a rare natural occurrence. It can also be made to happen artificially. For example, in a nuclear fission reaction, the parent nucleus releases neutrons as it splits into smaller nuclei.

This example shows the decay of helium-5 into helium-4.

$$^{5}_{2}\text{He} \longrightarrow\ ^{4}_{2}\text{He} + ^{1}_{0}\text{n}$$

Nuclear Equations

The emission of different types of nuclear radiation can cause a change in the mass and/or charge of the nucleus. Nuclear equations are used to demonstrate these changes.

Alpha Decay

Alpha decay causes the mass and charge of a nucleus to decrease. When the nucleus emits two protons and two neutrons, its atomic number reduces by two and its mass number reduces by four.

$$^{222}_{86}\text{radon} \longrightarrow\ ^{218}_{84}\text{polonium} + ^{4}_{2}\text{He}$$

In this example, the radon nucleus emits two protons and two neutrons to form a new polonium nucleus and a helium ion.

Beta Decay

Beta decay causes the charge of a nucleus to increase. When a neutron in the nucleus turns into a proton, its mass does not change. However, the addition of a new proton increases the charge of the nucleus.

$$^{14}_{6}\text{carbon} \longrightarrow\ ^{14}_{7}\text{nitrogen} + ^{0}_{-1}\text{e}$$

In this example, the carbon nucleus decays to form a nitrogen nucleus and a high-energy beta particle.

Gamma Decay

When some nuclei decay by alpha or beta particle emission, they also give out a gamma ray, to leave the nucleus in a more stable state. The gamma ray doesn't change the mass or charge of the nucleus.

$$^{137}_{55}\text{caesium-137} \longrightarrow\ ^{137}_{56}\text{barium-137} + ^{0}_{-1}\text{e} + ^{0}_{0}\gamma$$

In this example, the barium nucleus has excess energy, which is released in the form of a gamma ray.

Remember that the total mass and atomic number on each side of an equation must be equal.

Half-Lives & the Random Nature of Radioactive Decay

Radioactive decay is a completely random process that is not affected by external conditions such as temperature or pressure. Therefore, it is impossible to predict which nucleus in an isotope will decay next or when it will decay.

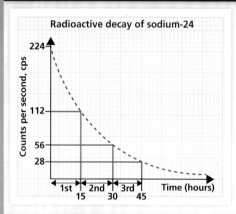

Radioactive decay of sodium-24

You can, however, measure the half-life, or the time it takes for the number of nuclei of the isotope in a sample to halve. You can use this to predict how long it will take for a radioactive source to decay.

The half-life of a radioactive isotope can also be the time it takes for the count rate (activity) from a sample containing the isotope to fall to half its initial level.

The number of unstable nuclei and the activity never reach zero. The time it takes for almost all the unstable nuclei to decay ranges from a millisecond to millions of years.

As shown in the graph, the half-life remains the same throughout the life of the sample.

Example: The initial count rate of a sample of sodium-24 is 224 counts per second (cps) or bequerels (Bq). Its half-life is 15 hours.

1 Calculate the fraction and the percentage of sodium-24 left after 45 hours.

After one half-life (15 h), the count rate decreases to 112 Bq.	$224 \div 2 = 112$
After two half-lives (30 h), the count rate decreases to 56 Bq.	$112 \div 2 = 56$
After three half-lives (45 h), the count rate decreases to 28 Bq.	$56 \div 2 = 28$
The reduction of sodium-24 from 224 Bq to 28 Bq is represented as a fraction.	$\dfrac{28}{224} = \dfrac{1}{8}$
This can be converted into a percentage.	$\dfrac{1}{8} = 0.125$ $0.125 \times 100 = 12.5\%$

2 Determine the ratio of the final count rate to the initial count rate after this time.

Determine the ratio of the final count rate to the initial count rate and reduce.	$28{:}224 = 1{:}8$

daydream
EDUCATION

Radioactive Contamination

The ionising radiation from a radioactive source can pass into living cells and ionise the atoms in them. The cells can be damaged or killed. As a result, there are significant risks when working with a radioactive source.

Irradiation

The exposure of an object to radiation is known as irradiation. Irradiated objects do not become radioactive, but suitable precautions must be taken to protect against any hazard that the radioactive source may present.

Sources of radiation can be kept in a lead-lined container or at a safe distance away from people. People in contact with radioactive materials can also wear protective clothing and monitor exposure by using a detector badge.

Fruit can be kept 'fresher' for longer by irradiating it with gamma radiation from a radioactive source such as cobalt-60.

The gamma rays destroy any bacteria without altering the fruit in any significant way (although this is subject to debate). Importantly, the process of irradiation does not make the fruit radioactive.

Medical instruments can also be sterilised in this way, especially if standard heat processes might melt the object.

Radioactive Contamination

Radioactive contamination is the unwanted presence of materials containing radioactive atoms on other materials. The radioactive atoms get onto or into an object. For example, you might touch a radioactive source without wearing gloves or breathe in a radioactive gas.

As the nuclei of the contaminating atoms decay, they release potentially dangerous radiation. The level of hazard from the contamination depends on the type of radiation emitted by the decaying nuclei.

Once an object has been contaminated, it is difficult to remove all the radioactive atoms, and the object will continue to be exposed to radiation.

Outside the body, beta- and gamma-emitting sources are the most dangerous because they can penetrate into your body and damage your cells and organs.

α Alpha particles are stopped by your skin so are less dangerous. However, inside the body, alpha radiation is the most dangerous because it has the biggest ionising effect. There is more risk of harm to our bodies from contamination by, rather than irradiation from, alpha-emitting sources.

β Beta-emitting sources are less damaging inside the body. Some radiation passes through the body.

γ Gamma-emitting sources are the least damaging inside the body. Most of the radiation passes through the body. These sources have the lowest ionising power.

It is important for research findings on the effects of radiation on humans to be published and shared among scientists so that the findings can be analysed by peer review.

daydream EDUCATION

Hazards & Uses of Radiation

Background Radiation

Background radiation is around us all the time. It comes from various sources, including:

- Natural sources such as rocks that contain radioactive uranium, thorium, radon and potassium
- Cosmic rays from space
- Man-made sources such as the fallout from nuclear weapons testing, nuclear accidents and medical x-rays.

Pie chart labels: Rocks & soil, Radon gas, Food & drink, Human activity, Cosmic rays

When working on radioactive experiments, scientists must always consider the amount of background radiation and exclude it from their results.

Radiation Dose

Radiation dose is a measure of the amount of radiation absorbed by a person and the medical effects of that radiation.

A person's background radiation exposure level and radiation dose received depend on various factors such as their location and occupation.

Radiation dose is measured in sieverts (Sv)

1000 millisieverts (mSv) = 1 sievert (Sv)

Irradiation is the process of being exposed to radiation.

Exposure (mSv)	Effects / Examples
10,000	Immediate illness; death likely within weeks
6,000	Typical dosage recorded in workers at the site of the Chernobyl disaster; death likely within a month
1,000	Radiation sickness; death unlikely
100	Recommended 5-year limit for radiation workers
10	Full-body CT scan
2	Typical annual radiation exposure
0.1	Chest X-ray

Half-Life of Radioactive Isotopes

The hazards associated with radioactive material also differ according to the half-life involved.

Sources with nuclei that are least unstable have the longest half-lives. They emit little radiation each second but do so for a long time.

Conversely, sources with very unstable nuclei decay quickly and have short half-lives, so they emit high levels of radiation for a short time.

Uranium-238, the most abundant isotope in uranium ore, decays with a half-life of 4.5 billion years. In contrast, hydrogen-7 has a half-life of 2.3×10^{-23} seconds.

daydream
EDUCATI

Medical Uses of Nuclear Radiation

Nuclear radiation is used in medicine to enable the exploration of internal organs and to control or destroy unwanted tissue.

Medical Tracers

Some radioactive isotopes can be used as tracers to help doctors examine inside the body. For example, iodine-123 is used to examine the functioning of the thyroid gland.

To test that the thyroid is working properly, some patients are given a sodium iodide tablet. Detectors are then used to determine whether the thyroid is correctly converting the iodine into thyroid hormones.

Iodine-123 emits low-energy gamma rays, which are highly penetrating and can escape the body without causing significant harm. It also has a short half-life (13 hours) which will give a high level of radioactivity for scanning before decaying quickly.

Gamma rays also have a low ionising power, which causes less damage to cells.

Radiotherapy

Radiation therapy, or **radiotherapy**, uses ionising radiation to destroy cancer cells or damage their DNA, stopping them from dividing and slowing their growth. Unfortunately, high levels of radiation also damage healthy cells. Therefore, it is vital to use the correct dosage and target the cancer carefully.

- **External beam radiotherapy** is given from outside the body. A machine outside the body aims high-energy gamma rays directly at the tumour.

- **Internal radiotherapy** involves placing a radioactive material inside the body to supply a high dose of radiation directly to the tumour.

Risks vs Benefits

It is important to evaluate the risks and benefits of nuclear radiation. For example, radiotherapy can make cancer patients very unwell, but it can also completely cure cancer.

In the period after the discovery of radioactivity, scientists did not understand the hazards of radiation. Marie Curie, who developed the theory of radioactivity, died from an illness most likely caused by long-term exposure to radiation.

Today, thanks to more than a century of scientific study and peer review of research, we now better understand the effects of radiation.

MARIE CURIE
1867–1934

45

Nuclear Fission & Fusion

Nuclear Fission

Nuclear fission is the splitting of a large and unstable nucleus of a material, such as uranium (U) or plutonium (Pu). Spontaneous fission is rare. Usually, for fission to occur, a nucleus must first absorb a neutron.

In fission, the nucleus usually splits into two smaller nuclei, roughly equal in size, and emits two or three neutrons. This reaction releases energy, most of which is transferred to the kinetic energy stores of the released neutrons; the remainder is carried away by gamma rays.

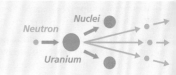

$$\,^{1}_{0}n + \,^{235}_{92}U \rightarrow \,^{236}_{92}U \rightarrow \,^{141}_{56}Ba + \,^{92}_{36}Kr + 3\,^{1}_{0}n + \text{energy}$$

Example: A neutron is absorbed by a uranium-235 nucleus. Fission occurs which leads to the formation of krypton-92 and barium-141, as well as the emission of three more neutrons. Krypton-92 and barium-141 are both radioactive and decay further by emitting beta particles.

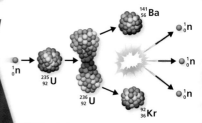

Chain Reaction

Each neutron produced by nuclear fission may be absorbed by another nucleus, and the process of nuclear fission may go on to start a chain reaction.

In a nuclear reactor, the energy released from nuclear fission chain reactions is used to heat water for thermal power generation.

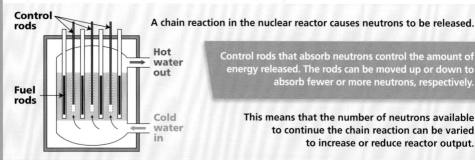

A chain reaction in the nuclear reactor causes neutrons to be released.

Control rods that absorb neutrons control the amount of energy released. The rods can be moved up or down to absorb fewer or more neutrons, respectively.

This means that the number of neutrons available to continue the chain reaction can be varied to increase or reduce reactor output.

In nuclear weapons, there is no control over the release of neutrons. This leads to an uncontrolled chain reaction and a huge explosion.

daydream

Nuclear Fusion

Nuclear fusion is the joining of two light nuclei to form a heavier nucleus.

During fusion, some of the mass of the nuclei may be converted into energy which is released by radiation.

As the nuclei approach each other, they repel one another because they have the same charge. The fusion of the nuclei happens quickly to prevent the repulsion of the charges from having time to stop the process.

It takes a huge amount of energy to force the two nuclei together.

In the middle of the Sun, the immense pressure and a temperature approaching 15 million degrees Celsius generates a plasma in which hydrogen nuclei fuse into helium nuclei.

We try to recreate these conditions for nuclear fusion on Earth by using intense magnetic fields, powerful lasers or ion beams.

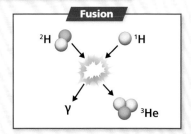

Fusion

^{2}H ^{1}H

γ ^{3}He

	Nuclear Fission	Nuclear Fusion
Definition	Splitting the nucleus of a large atom into two or more smaller nuclei	Fusing together the nuclei of two or more light atoms into a heavy nucleus
Where does it take place?	In nuclear fission reactors	In stars, including the Sun
What is needed for the reaction to occur?	A sufficient amount of the substance to create a chain reaction High-speed neutrons	Very high temperature and pressure
What are the energy requirements?	Requires little energy to split the nucleus	Requires extremely high energy to bring two or more nuclei close enough that nuclear forces can overcome their electrostatic repulsion
How much energy is released?	Releases a million times more energy than a chemical reaction	Releases three or four times more energy than nuclear fission

Forces

A force is a push or pull that acts on an object as a result of the object's interaction with another object. Forces are invisible interactions between objects that lead to visible effects such as acceleration.

Scalars and Vectors

A scalar has magnitude (size) only, whereas a vector has magnitude and direction. Forces are vector quantities.

Imagine two cars are travelling at the same speed. If they are travelling in different directions, they have different velocities. This is because velocity is a vector quantity that measures magnitude and direction.

Scalars	Vectors
Speed	Velocity
Distance	Acceleration
Mass	Displacement
Energy	Force

Contact and Non-Contact Forces

Some forces require objects to be in contact (touching) for the forces to interact. For example, friction acts against the movement of two objects rubbing against each other.

Some forces, such as gravity, are non-contact forces that act at a distance.

Contact Forces	Non-Contact Forces
Friction	Gravitational
Air resistance	Electrostatic
Tension	Magnetic

Mass, Gravity and Weight

Mass	Mass is the amount of matter in something. The mass of an object is the same anywhere in the universe.
Gravity	Gravity is the force of attraction between all matter. It varies depending on location. As the distance between two objects increases, the force of gravity between them decreases. All objects have a gravitational force, but gravitational force is directly proportional to mass, so objects with a larger mass also exert a larger gravitational force. An object that is double the mass of another object exerts twice as much gravitational pull.
Weight	Weight is the force acting on an object because of gravity. The weight of an object depends on its mass as well as on the strength of the gravitational field at the point where the object is.

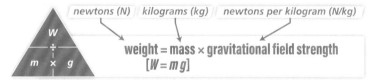

newtons (N)　kilograms (kg)　newtons per kilogram (N/kg)

$$W \div (m \times g)$$

weight = mass × gravitational field strength
$$[W = m\,g]$$

The weight of an object and the mass of an object are directly proportional: $W \propto m$

The force of gravity close to the Earth is due to its gravitational field. Near the Earth's surface, g is approximately 9.8 N/kg so each kilogram has a gravitational pull of 9.8 N acting on it. The examples below show how the weight of an object varies depending on its location.

Earth
$m = 75$ kg
$g = 9.8$ N/kg
$W = 735$ N

Moon
$m = 75$ kg
$g = 1.6$ N/kg
$W = 120$ N

Mars
$m = 75$ kg
$g = 3.7$ N/kg
$W = 277.5$ N

daydream EDUCATION

The weight of an object can be measured by using a newtonmeter (a calibrated spring balance). The spring is pulled down by the object whose weight is being measured.

The weight of an object is considered to act through a single point, known as its centre of mass.

Free Body Diagrams

Vector quantities may be represented as arrows, such as in free body diagrams.

The length of each arrow represents the magnitude of the force.

The direction of each arrow represents the direction of the force.

Lift

Thrust

Drag

Weight

Resultant Forces

Multiple forces acting on an object may be replaced by a single force that has the same effect as all the original forces. This single force is called the resultant force.

When forces are balanced, the resultant force is zero. A stationary object will remain stationary, and a moving object will continue at the same speed.

If the resultant force is not zero, a stationary object will begin to move in the direction of the resultant force. In contrast, a moving object will speed up, slow down or change direction based on the direction of the resultant force.

$$5N - 5N = 0N$$

$$10N - 5N = 5N$$

A single force can also be split or 'resolved' into two components acting at right angles to each other. Usually one acts horizontally and the other vertically.

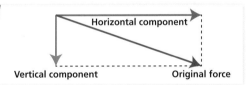

Horizontal component

Vertical component

Original force

Calculating Resultant Forces

If the individual forces are not in the same plane, then the resultant force can be found by using a scale diagram.

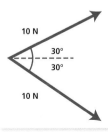

10 N

30°

30°

10 N

Use a ruler and a protractor to make a scale drawing of the forces. Use a sensible scale (e.g. 1 cm per 1 N).

The resultant force is found by adding the two separate forces one after the other (tip to tail) and measuring the total distance (the length of the dashed line).

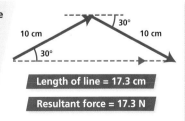

10 cm

30°

10 cm

30°

Length of line = 17.3 cm

Resultant force = 17.3 N

Forces & Elasticity

Applying a force to an object causes it to move in the direction of the applied force. However, in order to stretch, compress or bend a stationary object, more than one force is needed.

If an object goes back to its original shape and length after the forces acting upon it have been removed, it has been **elastically deformed**. If an object does not return to its original shape and length after the forces have been removed, it has been **inelastically deformed**.

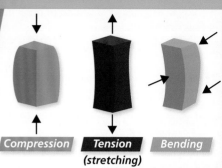

Compression   **Tension**   **Bending**
(stretching)

The extension of an elastic object, such as a spring, is directly proportional to the force applied provided that the limit of proportionality is not exceeded.

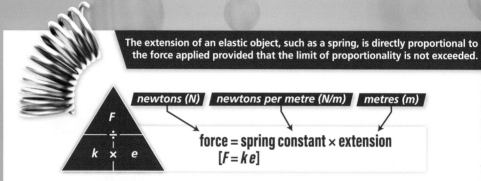

newtons (N)   newtons per metre (N/m)   metres (m)

$$F = \frac{F}{k \times e}$$

force = spring constant × extension
$[F = ke]$

If an object is compressed, the same relationship applies, with e denoting compression.

When forces stretch or compress a spring, work is done and energy is transferred to the elastic potential energy store of the spring. If it is elastically deformed, then all of the energy has been transferred into this store and is equal to the work done on the object.

The work done in stretching or compressing a spring (up to the limit of proportionality) can be calculated by using the following equation:

elastic potential energy = 0.5 × spring constant × (extension)²

$$E_e = \frac{1}{2} ke^2$$

As long as the spring has not been inelastically deformed, the work done on the spring and the elastic potential energy stored are equal. If the limit of proportionality is exceeded, the spring becomes permanently deformed and will not return to its original shape and length.

daydream
EDUCATIO

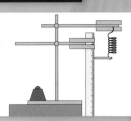

Practical Activity: Investigate the relationship between force and extension for a spring.

The following practical activity can be used to show the proportional relationship between force and extension (Hooke's law).

1 Set up your apparatus as shown in the diagram.
Make sure of the following:

- The ruler is vertical. It is helpful if the zero on the metre ruler is at the same height as the top of the spring.
- The pointer is horizontal, attached securely to the bottom of the spring and rests against the scale of the ruler.

2 Measure the length of the spring before any mass has been added, and record it in a results table like the one shown:

Weight (N)	Length of spring (cm)	Extension of spring (cm)
0		
1		

3 Hook a 100g mass hanger onto the spring. Each time a mass is added to the hanger, you will need to convert it to newtons. A 100g mass exerts a force of approximately 1.0 N.

4 Measure and record the reading on the ruler – that is, the length of the spring when a force of 1.0 N is applied to it.

5 Calculate the extension of the spring.

6 Add further 100g masses to the hanger, and measure and record the length of the spring each time in the table. You also need to calculate and record the extension for each weight.

7 Analyse your results.

a) Use your results to plot a graph with 'Extension (cm)' on the x-axis and 'Weight (N)' on the y-axis. It should give a straight line through the origin.

b) State the relationship between force and extension of the spring.

c) Calculate the spring constant by using the equation:

force = spring constant × extension

d) Calculate the work done in stretching the spring by using the equation:

elastic potential energy = 0.5 × spring constant × (extension)²

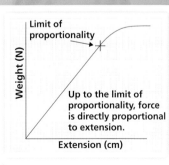

Up to the limit of proportionality, force is directly proportional to extension.

Work Done & Energy Transfer

Work is done on an object when a force causes the object to move through a distance. If the object does not move, no work is done.

The work done by a force on an object can be calculated by using the following equation:

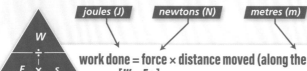

joules (J) newtons (N) metres (m)

work done = force × distance moved (along the line of action of the force)
$$[W = Fs]$$

(Triangle: W over $F \times s$)

One joule of work is done when a force of one newton causes a displacement of one metre:

1 joule = 1 newton-metre

Work done against the frictional forces acting on an object causes the object's temperature to rise.

The kinetic energy store of the moving object is transferred to its internal (thermal) energy store.

Example

If a horse pulls a cart with a force of 220 N at a constant speed and covers a distance of 10 m, it is doing work:

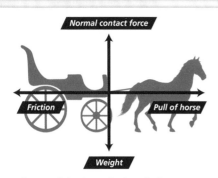

Normal contact force

Friction

Pull of horse

Weight

work done = force × distance moved

$$= 220 × 10$$

$$= 2{,}200 \text{ N-m or } 2{,}200 \text{ J}$$

Some of the horse's chemical energy store is transferred to the cart's kinetic energy store and the internal (thermal) energy store.

daydream
EDUCATION

Moments

A force or a system of forces may cause an object to rotate. The turning effect of a force about a pivot is called the moment of the force.

The size of the moment is calculated by the equation:

newton-metres (Nm) newtons (N) metres (m)

$$\text{moment of a force} = \text{force} \times \text{distance}$$

$$M = Fd$$

Distance is the perpendicular distance from the pivot to the line of action of the force.

As the force applied, or the perpendicular distance of the force from the pivot increases, so does the moment of the force.

Undoing a nut by hand is difficult because you cannot generate enough force to cause the nut to rotate. However, by using a spanner or wrench, you can increase the perpendicular distance from the nut (pivot) and thus the size of the turning effect of the force (moment).

To achieve the maximum moment, force needs to be applied perpendicularly to the spanner, which is the line of action.

In this example, 20 N of force is applied to the spanner 20 cm from the nut (pivot).

Moment of a force = Force × Distance

$$M = 20 \text{ N} \times 0.2 \text{ m}$$

$$M = 4.0 \text{ Nm}$$

20 cm = 0.2 m

Axis of rotation — Nut

20 cm

Spanner

Force = 20 N

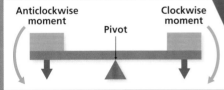

Anticlockwise moment

Clockwise moment

Pivot

The masses on either side of the see-saw balance. The total clockwise moment about the pivot equals the total anticlockwise moment about the pivot.

If each side has more than one mass, the moments are added to determine the total moment.

The see-saw opposite is balanced. Find the force applied by F_3.

$$\frac{\text{Total anticlockwise}}{\text{moment}} = \frac{\text{Total clockwise}}{\text{moment}}$$

$$(3 \times 0.45) + (15 \times 0.2) = (F_3 \times 0.3) + (3.5 \times 0.6)$$

$$1.35 + 3 = (F_3 \times 0.3) + 2.1$$

$$1.35 + 3 - 2.1 = F_3 \times 0.3$$

$$\frac{1.35 + 3 - 2.1}{0.3} = F_3$$

$$F_3 = 7.5 \text{ N}$$

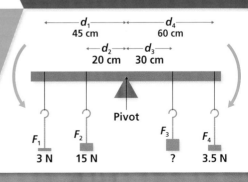

d_1 45 cm d_4 60 cm

d_2 20 cm d_3 30 cm

Pivot

F_1 F_2 F_3 F_4

3 N 15 N ? 3.5 N

Levers & Gears

Simple lever or gear systems can be used to transmit the rotational effects of forces.

Levers

Levers are mechanical devices that make doing **work** easier. They reduce the force needed to move an object by increasing the distance over which the force is applied. This reduces the force required to generate the necessary moment, making moving or lifting a load easier.

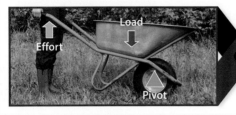

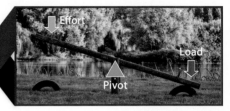

Gears

Gears are toothed wheels attached to shafts. They are used to transmit power and rotational motion around mechanical systems.

Gear trains consist of two or more interlocking gears. If the driver (input) gear rotates clockwise, the driven (output) gear rotates anticlockwise and vice versa.

Changing Speed

Gears can be used to make the output speed faster or slower than the input speed by using different-sized gears.

Creating a Faster Output Speed

To make the output speed faster, the input gear must be larger than the output gear.

Input gear (40 teeth) — Output gear (20 teeth)

Creating a Slower Output Speed

To make the output speed slower, the input gear must be smaller than the output gear.

Input gear (10 teeth) — Output gear (30 teeth)

Calculating Gear Ratios

The larger gear always equals 1. The smaller gear is calculated by dividing the number of teeth on the larger gear by the number of teeth on the smaller gear.

In the example above:

Input = 1	Gear Ratio 1 : 2	Output = 40 ÷ 20 = 2

1 turn of the driver gear = 2 turns of the driven gear

In the example above:

Input = 30 ÷ 10 = 3	Gear Ratio 3 : 1	Output = 1

3 turns of the driver gear = 1 turn of the driven gear

daydream
EDUCATION

Pressure & Pressure Differences in Fluids

The particles in fluids move around freely, enabling a fluid to flow.
A fluid can be either a liquid or a gas.

Pressure in Fluids

As the particles in a fluid move around, they collide with each other and with the surface of their container. This exerts a force on the surfaces.

The force per unit area is pressure.

Pressure in fluids causes a force normal (at right angles) to any surface that it pushes against.

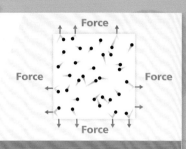

Force

Force   Force

Force

The pressure at the surface of a fluid is calculated with the equation:

pascals (Pa) ➡ $$\text{pressure} = \frac{\text{force normal to surface of area}}{\text{area of that surface}}$$

newtons (N)

metres squared (m²)

$$p = \frac{F}{A}$$

Pressure in a Column of Liquid

Density

Under set conditions, the density of a liquid is the same throughout, or uniform, regardless of its size or shape. The density of water is approximately 1,000 kg/m³.

A dense liquid exerts greater pressure than a less dense liquid because it contains more particles in a given volume. Therefore, there are more particles to collide with the surfaces of objects within the liquid, creating a greater force per unit area.

Depth

Although a liquid has uniform density, the pressure in a column of liquid increases with depth. This is because there is a greater weight of particles from above as you get deeper.

This image demonstrates how pressure varies with depth. The water at the bottom of the tank is under the greatest pressure, so it is pushed from the tank at the greatest force, creating the strongest jet of water.

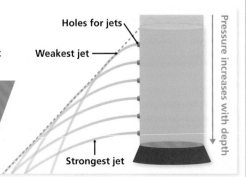

Holes for jets

Weakest jet

Pressure increases with depth

Strongest jet

The pressure due to a column of liquid is calculated with the equation:

pascals (Pa)   kilograms per metre cubed (kg/m³)

pressure = column height × density of liquid × gravitational field strength

$p = h \rho g$ metres (m)   newtons per kilogram (N/kg)

Example

A scuba diver swims to a depth of 15 m.
He then descends to 35 m.

Given that the density of sea-water is 1,030 kg/m³,
calculate the difference in pressure between
15 m and 35 m.

Pressure at 15 m

$p = h \rho g$

$= 15 \times 1{,}030 \times 9.8$

$= 151{,}410$ Pa

Pressure at 35 m

$p = h \rho g$

$= 35 \times 1{,}030 \times 9.8$

$= 353{,}290$ Pa

Difference in Pressure

$= 353{,}290 - 151{,}410$

$= 201{,}880$ Pa

$= 2.0 \times 10^5$ Pa (to 2 s.f.)

Upthrust

When an object is fully or partially submerged in a fluid,
it displaces a volume of fluid equal to its volume, and the
fluid exerts a force on the object in every direction.

However, because pressure increases with depth,
there is a greater pressure acting on the object's
bottom surface than on its top surface.

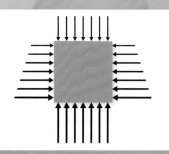

This difference in pressure creates a resultant upward force, known as upthrust,
which is equal to the weight of the fluid that has been displaced by the object.

Upthrust = Weight of object ➡️ **Up and down forces are balanced so the object will float.**

Upthrust < Weight of object ➡️ **Down force is greater than up force so the object will sink.**

The upthrust on an object increases as it is submerged into the water.

The density of an object determines whether it sinks or floats. An object that is less dense than the surrounding fluid will float, and an object that is denser than the surrounding fluid will sink.

Box A is filled with air, so it is less dense than the surrounding water. This also means that it weighs less than the equivalent volume of water that it would displace if completely underwater.

Upthrust is greater than the weight of box A so the box floats.

Box B is filled with sand, so it is denser than the surrounding water. This also means that it weighs more than the equivalent volume of water that it would displace if completely underwater.

Upthrust is less than the weight of box B so the box sinks.

When an object is less dense than the surrounding fluid and floats, it only displaces a volume of fluid equivalent to its weight.

The box's weight is equivalent to the weight of this volume of water.

The atmosphere is a thin layer of air around Earth that gets **less dense** with **increasing altitude**. Air molecules colliding with a surface create atmospheric pressure.

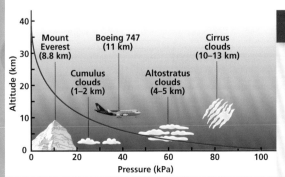

Mount Everest (8.8 km)

Boeing 747 (11 km)

Cirrus clouds (10–13 km)

Cumulus clouds (1–2 km)

Altostratus clouds (4–5 km)

Altitude (km) / Pressure (kPa)

Atmospheric pressure decreases as altitude increases because:

- The number of air molecules decreases, leaving fewer molecules to collide with surfaces.

- With fewer air molecules, the weight of air decreases.

- There is a smaller column of air above the surface.

Forces and Motion

Distance and Displacement

Distance

Distance is how far an object moves. It is a scalar quantity because it does not involve direction.

Displacement

Displacement is a vector quantity that includes the distance an object moves and the direction in which it moves. It is measured in a straight line from the starting point to the finish point.

If you walk 2 km west and then 2 km east, you have travelled a total distance of 4 km. However, your displacement is 0 km.

Example

Elise ran 5 km as shown by the dotted line A to B.

Her displacement is 3 km east.

Distance

A   Displacement   B

Speed and Velocity

Speed is the rate at which someone or something moves. It is a scalar quantity because it does not involve direction. Objects rarely travel at a constant speed. When people walk, run or travel in a car, their speed changes constantly.

metres per second (m/s)   metres (m)

$$\text{speed} = \frac{\text{distance}}{\text{time}}$$

$$[v = \frac{s}{t}]$$

seconds (s)

$$\begin{array}{c} s \\ \div \\ v \times t \end{array}$$

Example

It took Max 5 minutes to drive to the cinema. His mean speed was 15 m/s. How far did Max drive?

$$\text{distance} = \text{speed} \times \text{time}$$
$$= 15 \times (5 \times 60)$$
$$= 4,500 \text{ m}$$

Max drove 4,500 metres, or 4.5 kilometres.

Typical Values of Speed

A person's speed depends upon the individual's age and health, the mode of transport, the terrain being travelled and the length of the journey.

A healthy adult can walk at 1.5 m/s, run at 3 m/s and cycle at 6 m/s.

A car travelling at 30 mph moves at 13 m/s.

The speed of sound in air is 330 m/s, but this can vary.

daydream EDUCATION

Distance-Time Graphs

If an object moves along a straight line, the distance travelled can be represented by a distance-time graph.

gradient of graph = speed
The steeper the graph, the faster the speed.

$$speed = \frac{distance}{time}$$

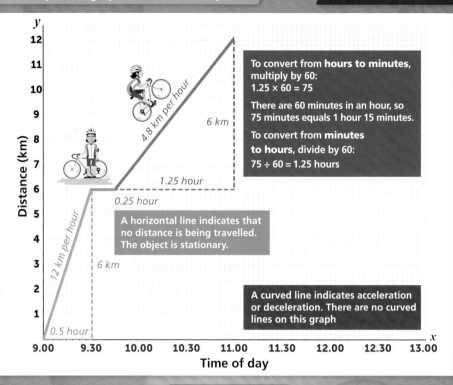

To convert from **hours to minutes**, multiply by 60:
$1.25 \times 60 = 75$

There are 60 minutes in an hour, so 75 minutes equals 1 hour 15 minutes.

To convert from **minutes to hours**, divide by 60:
$75 \div 60 = 1.25$ hours

A horizontal line indicates that no distance is being travelled. The object is stationary.

A curved line indicates acceleration or deceleration. There are no curved lines on this graph

Calculating Speed

To calculate speed at a specific point on a distance-time graph, you can draw a tangent to the curve and then measure the gradient of the tangent.

$$gradient = \frac{change\ in\ y}{change\ in\ x}$$
$$= \frac{200-170}{18-12}$$
$$= \frac{30}{6}$$
$$= 5\ m/s$$

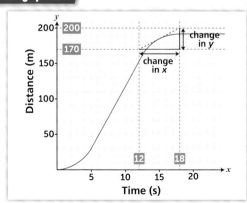

Acceleration

Acceleration is the rate of change of velocity with time. If an object is slowing down, this is called deceleration. If an object is moving in a circular path at a constant speed, then it is still accelerating because of the change in direction.

metres per second squared (m/s²)

metres per second (m/s)

seconds (s)

$$acceleration = \frac{change\ in\ velocity}{time}$$

$$a = \frac{\triangle v}{t}$$

Example

An F1 car decelerates from 69 m/s to 25 m/s in 1.2 seconds.

Calculate the deceleration of the car.

$$acceleration = \frac{change\ in\ velocity}{time}$$

$$= \frac{25-69}{1.2}$$

$$= \frac{-44}{1.2}$$

$$= -36.7\ m/s^2\ (3\ s.f.)$$

Uniform Acceleration

The following equation applies to uniform acceleration:

m/s   m/s   m/s²   m

(final velocity)² − (initial velocity)² = 2 × acceleration × distance

$$[v^2 - u^2 = 2as]$$

Example

An aeroplane accelerates uniformly from 120 m/s to 240 m/s. During this time, it travels 2 km.

Calculate the aeroplane's acceleration during this period.

$$v^2 - u^2 = 2as$$

$$240^2 - 120^2 = 2 \times a \times 2{,}000$$

$$57{,}600 - 14{,}400 = a \times 4{,}000$$

$$a = \frac{57{,}600 - 14{,}400}{4{,}000}$$

$$a = 10.8\ m/s^2$$

daydrea
EDUCATE

Velocity-Time Graphs

Velocity-time graphs show how an object's velocity changes over time.

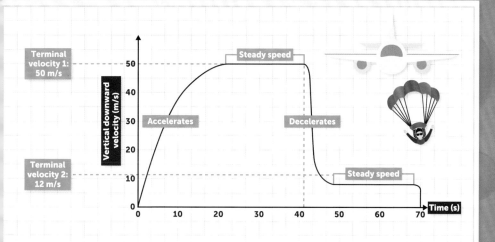

Terminal velocity 1: 50 m/s

Terminal velocity 2: 12 m/s

Vertical downward velocity (m/s)

Steady speed

Accelerates

Decelerates

Steady speed

Time (s)

1 A skydiver jumps out of a plane and accelerates due to the force of gravity.

2 As the skydiver speeds up, air resistance increases. This causes the resultant force acting on the skydiver to decrease. The acceleration of the skydiver also decreases.

3 At terminal velocity 1, the force of air resistance (drag) is equal to the force of gravity so the resultant force (and acceleration) is zero.

4 The skydiver deploys her parachute, increasing air resistance and slowing her down.

5 The skydiver's speed continues to slow until the force of air resistance is equal to the force of gravity and terminal velocity 2 is reached.

6 The skydiver lands and decelerates to a halt (rest) in a very short time. The steep graph line shows a large deceleration.

Near the Earth's surface, any object falling freely under gravity has an acceleration of 9.8 m/s^2. For most objects, this acceleration does not remain constant as the object's speed increases and decreases regularly.

When a velocity-time graph is made up of straight lines, the total distance travelled can be calculated by splitting the area into shapes, working out their areas and adding them together.

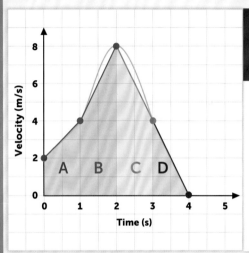

When a graph has curved lines, the total distance travelled is estimated by roughly splitting the area into trapeziums and adding their areas together.

Area A: $\frac{1}{2} \times (2 + 4) \times 1 = 3$

Area B: $\frac{1}{2} \times (4 + 8) \times 1 = 6$

Area C: $\frac{1}{2} \times (8 + 4) \times 1 = 6$

Area D: $\frac{1}{2} \times (4 + 0) \times 1 = 2$

_____

Total: $= 17$

The total distance travelled is 17 m.

The total area under the curved line is likely to be an underestimate because the combined size of the trapeziums is smaller than the actual size of the area under the line.

You can also estimate the total distance travelled by counting the number of squares under the graph and then multiplying this by the distance that each square represents.

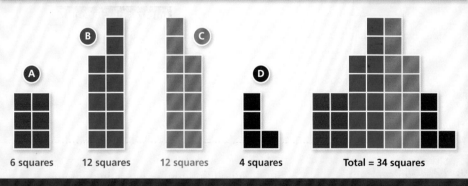

A	B	C	D	Total
6 squares	12 squares	12 squares	4 squares	Total = 34 squares

Distance represented by 1 square: distance = **velocity** × **time** = 1 × 0.5 = 0.5 m

Total distance travelled = **34 × 0.5 = 17 m**

daydrea

Newton's Laws of Motion

Newton's laws describe the relationship between an object and the forces acting upon it, and its motion in response to those forces.

Newton's First Law

If the resultant force acting on an object is zero, the forces acting upon it are balanced. This means its acceleration will be zero and its velocity (speed and/or direction) constant. Therefore:

A stationary object will remain stationary.

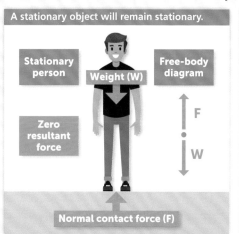

Stationary person

Weight (W)

Free-body diagram

Zero resultant force

F

W

Normal contact force (F)

A moving object will continue to move at a constant speed in the same direction. When a vehicle travels at a steady speed, the resistive forces (friction) balance the driving force (thrust).

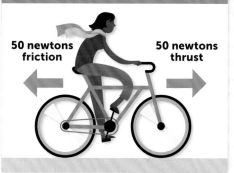

50 newtons friction

50 newtons thrust

Every object has inertia. This is its tendency to continue in a state of rest or uniform motion.

Newton's Second Law

For an object to accelerate (and start moving, stop, speed up, slow down or change direction), the forces acting upon it need to be unbalanced: there needs to be a resultant force.

The acceleration of an object depends on its mass and the resultant force acting on it. This relationship can be represented by the following equation:

newtons (N)   **kilograms (kg)**   **metres per second squared (m/s²)**

resultant force = mass × acceleration

$$F = m\,a$$

The acceleration of an object is proportional to the resultant force acting on it: $a \propto F.$

The greater the resultant force acting on an object, the greater the object's acceleration. For example, pedalling a bike faster (i.e. increasing the driving force) increases acceleration.

The acceleration of an object is inversely proportional to the mass of the object: $a \propto \frac{1}{m}.$

An object with a large mass will have a slower rate of acceleration than an object with a small mass if the same force is applied. For example, a greater force is required to push a car than a bike with the same rate of acceleration, because much more force is needed to overcome the car's inertia.

Calculate the resultant force needed to make a car of mass 800 kg accelerate at 4 m/s².	$F = ma$ $F = 800 \times 4 = 3{,}200$ N
When the car is fully loaded, its mass is 1,200 kg. What resultant force is needed to provide the same acceleration?	$F = ma$ $F = 1{,}200 \times 4 = 4{,}800$ N

The loaded car has a bigger mass than the unloaded car. It therefore needs a bigger force to give it the same acceleration as the unloaded car.

The ratio of force to acceleration is called **inertial mass**: $m = \dfrac{F}{a}$

It is a measure of how difficult it is to change the velocity of an object.

Practical Activity 1

Investigate the effect of varying the force on the acceleration of an object of constant mass.

In this practical activity, you will time how long it takes for a trolley of constant mass to move a distance when different forces are applied.

1 Set up your apparatus as shown.
- Use a ruler to measure 20 cm intervals on the bench, and draw straight lines in chalk at these intervals.
- Attach the pulley to the end of the bench.
- Tie a length of string to the trolley. Pass the string over the pulley, and attach it to the weight stack.

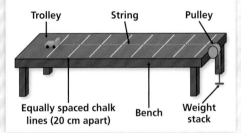

2 Attach 1.0 N to the weight stack, and hold the trolley at the start point.

3 Release the trolley, and as you do, start a stopwatch. Press the stopwatch (lap mode) as the trolley passes each interval on the bench.

4 Create a table like this one and record the results.

Distance Travelled (cm)	1.0 N	0.8 N	0.6 N	0.4 N	0.2 N
			Time (s)		
20					
40					
...					

5 Repeat step 3 with decreasing amounts of weight, and record your results in the table. Place the weights removed from the stack on top of the trolley each time you decrease the weight. This ensures the mass of the system stays the same.

daydrea EDUCAT

Practical Activity 2

Investigate the effect of varying the mass of an object on the acceleration produced by a constant force.

1 Set up your apparatus as in Practical Activity 1.

2 Select a constant weight for the weight stack, and attach it to the stack.

3 Put a 100 g (0.1 kg) mass on the trolley, and hold it at the start point.

4 Release the trolley, and as you do, start a stopwatch. Press the stopwatch (lap mode) as the trolley passes each interval on the bench.

5 Create a table like the one shown and record the results.

Distance Travelled (cm)	Mass of Trolley (kg)				
	0.1	0.2	...		
20					
40					
...					

6 Repeat step 3 with increasing amounts of mass on the trolley, and record your results in the table.

The results from both activities should confirm the equation linked to Newton's second law: $F = m\,a$.

Newton's Third Law

When two objects interact, the forces they exert on each other are equal and opposite. When an object exerts a force on a second object, the second object exerts the same amount of force on the first object. This is a force pair.

When you push against a wall, the wall pushes back with an equal force. Only the friction between your feet and the floor stops you from moving away from the wall.

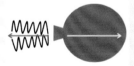

When air is released from a balloon, it pushes against the outside air, and the outside air pushes back. As a result, the balloon is propelled forward by the opposing force. This opposing force is known as thrust.

The balloon moves forward as the thrust causes it to accelerate.

It is important to remember that equal forces do not always have the same effect. For example, when a gun is fired, the gun exerts a force on the bullet that pushes it forward, but the bullet also exerts an equal force on the gun that pushes it backwards. However, because the gun's inertial mass is larger than that of the bullet, the gun moves backwards only a small distance.

If the two forces are acting on the same object – for example, a box – it is not an example of Newton's third law. These two forces are not a force pair because they are acting on the same object, the box.

Normal contact force

Weight

daydream EDUCATION

65

Forces & Braking

When a driver performs an emergency stop, the time and distance it takes for the vehicle to stop depend on the distance the vehicle travels during the driver's reaction time (thinking distance) and the distance it takes for the braking force to stop the vehicle (braking distance).

stopping distance = thinking distance + braking distance

For a given braking force, the greater the speed of the vehicle, the greater the stopping distance

Braking Distance

Braking distance is affected by multiple factors.

Tyre Condition

Tyre condition affects the traction between a car and the road. Bald tyres do not have much traction with the road, resulting in long stopping distances.

Worn or Faulty Brakes

Worn or faulty brakes can increase a vehicle's stopping distance. This is because they require a greater input force to achieve the same stopping distance as well-maintained brakes.

Adverse Weather

Adverse weather and resulting poor road conditions can reduce the traction between a car and the road. Ice, water and oil can all increase stopping distances.

When a driver applies a force to the brakes, work done by the friction between the brakes and the wheels reduces the wheels' kinetic energy. Energy is transferred from the wheels' kinetic energy store to the brakes' thermal energy store, increasing their temperature.

The greater the speed of a vehicle, the greater the braking force needed to stop the vehicle in a certain distance.

The greater the braking force, the greater the deceleration of the vehicle. Large decelerations may lead to brakes overheating and/or loss of control (skidding).

daydrea
EDUCATE

Speed

There are several factors that can affect the stopping distance of a car.

Speed has a huge influence on stopping distance.

Thinking Distance	Braking Distance	
30 mph (13 m/s)	9 m	14 m → 23 m
50 mph (22 m/s)	15 m	38 m → 53 m
70 mph (31 m/s)	21 m	75 m → 96 m

Braking Distance — Condition of tyres, Mass, Road surface, Condition of brakes

Speed

Thinking Distance — Drugs, Alcohol, Tiredness, Distractions

Key m = metres   m/s = metres per second   mph = miles per hour

Thinking Distance

Thinking distance is affected by the speed of the vehicle and the driver's reaction time.

Reaction times vary from person to person, from 0.2 s to 0.9 s, and can be affected by drugs, alcohol, tiredness and distractions, such as mobile phones. If the car is travelling at 10 m/s, a reaction time of 0.2 s means the thinking distance is 10 × 0.2 = 2 m. A reaction time of 0.9 s means the thinking distance is 10 × 0.9 = 9 m.

The ruler drop test is used to measure reaction times.

As your partner holds the ruler, stand with your hand in front of you, and position the ruler between your index finger and thumb. The top of your finger should be level with 0 cm on the ruler.

As your partner drops the ruler, catch it as quickly as possible. Measure the point at which you caught the ruler from the top of your thumb.

Repeat three times, and take an average of your results. Typical data for the test is shown below.

Excellent	Good	Average	Fair	Poor
<7.5 cm	<16 cm	<20 cm	<28 cm	>28 cm

Momentum

Momentum is a property of moving objects. It is a vector (has magnitude and direction). The greater the velocity and/or mass of the object, the greater its momentum.

kilogram metre per second (kg m/s) | kilograms (kg) | metres per second (m/s)

momentum = mass × velocity

$$p = mv$$

Example

A 120 kg rugby player is running at 9 m/s. Calculate his momentum.

$p = mv$
$= 120 \times 9$
$= 1{,}080$

The rugby player's momentum is 1,080 kg m/s.

Conservation of Momentum

In a closed system (a system with no external forces), the overall momentum before an event is equal to the overall momentum after the event. This is called the law of conservation of momentum.

1. Trolley A is moving left to right at 2.0 m/s. It collides head on with trolley B, which is stationary. Trolley A stops dead, and trolley B moves to the right. Calculate the final velocity of trolley B.

30 kg   2.0 m/s   22 kg   ?

A   B

1 Calculate the overall momentum before and after the collision.

Overall momentum before collision = **Overall momentum after collision**
p of trolley A: $30 \times 2.0 = 60$ p of trolley A: 0
p of trolley B: 0 p of trolley B: $22 \times v = 60$

2 Rearrange the momentum equation for trolley B after the event to calculate its velocity.

$22 \times v = 60$
$v = \dfrac{60}{22}$
$= 2.7$ m/s (2 s.f.)

2. While travelling east, a small car with a mass of 950 kg is involved in a head-on collision with a large car travelling west. The large car has a mass of 2,000 kg. Both cars come to a dead stop in the collision. If the large car was travelling west at a speed of 13 m/s (velocity = -13 m/s), what was the speed of the small car?

1 Calculate the overall momentum before and after the collision.

Overall momentum before collision = **Overall momentum after collision**
p of small car: $950 \times v = 950\,v$ kg m/s p of small car: 0
p of large car: $2{,}000 \times (-13$ m/s$) = -26{,}000$ kg m/s p of large car: 0

2 The total momentum before an event is equal to the total momentum after the event, so:

$950\,v + (-26{,}000) = 0$
$950\,v = 26{,}000$
$v = \dfrac{26{,}000}{950}$
$= 27$ m/s (2 s.f.) (moving east)

daydream EDUCATIO

Changes in Momentum

The momentum of an object changes when a (non-zero resultant) force acts on it.
The larger the applied force, the greater the change in momentum.

Combining Newton's second law equation, $F = ma$, with the equation for the acceleration of an object changing speed, $a = \frac{\Delta v}{t}$, provides the rate of change in momentum, which is measured as a force.

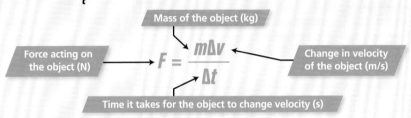

Mass of the object (kg)

Force acting on the object (N) → $F = \dfrac{m\Delta v}{\Delta t}$ ← Change in velocity of the object (m/s)

Time it takes for the object to change velocity (s)

The greater the change in momentum, the greater the force.

Safety Features

Many products have safety features that are designed to reduce the rate of change in momentum – specifically deceleration – and thus the force acting on the user.

Car airbags inflate when a car crashes in order to reduce the rate of deceleration of any occupants more gradually.

Seat belts stretch to reduce the wearer's rate of deceleration.

Cycling helmets contain an inner layer of foam to increase the time it takes for a wearer's head to stop in a collision. This reduces the rate of deceleration and, therefore, the force acting on the head.

Cushioned playground surfaces and **gym crash mats** are made with soft, compressible materials to increase the time it takes for users to decelerate to rest when they land after falling.

1 A gymnast with mass of 55 kg performs a vault and lands on a crash mat at a speed of 5 m/s.

Calculate the gymnast's momentum as he hits the mat.

momentum = mass × velocity
= 55 × 5
= 275 kg m/s

Final momentum = 0

Change in momentum = 0 – 275
= –275 kg m/s

2 After hitting the crash mat, the gymnast slows down and stops in 0.2 seconds.

Calculate the force exerted by the ground on the gymnast.

$F = \dfrac{m\Delta v}{\Delta t}$

$= \dfrac{-275}{0.2}$

= –1,375 N (a decelerating force)

Waves

Waves carry energy, as well as information, from one place to another. They may be either longitudinal or transverse.

Energy Transfer

When waves travel through a medium, they set up regular patterns of disturbance. The particles of the medium oscillate (move back and forth in a regular rhythm) to transfer energy from one point to another without transferring matter.

For example, when a pebble is dropped into water, the water appears to move outward from the spot where the pebble hit it. However, the water itself does not travel outward, but the waves do.

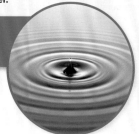

To further explain this, imagine a bird sat on the water. As the water ripples outward, the bird does not move in the same direction as the waves; it stays in the same place, bobbing up and down on top of the water.

Longitudinal Waves

In longitudinal waves, the oscillations are parallel to the direction of energy transfer.

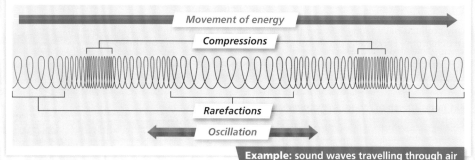

Movement of energy

Compressions

Rarefactions

Oscillation

Example: sound waves travelling through air

Transverse Waves

In transverse waves, the oscillations are at right angles (perpendicular) to the direction of energy transfer.

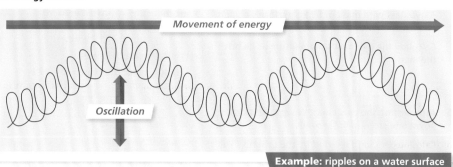

Movement of energy

Oscillation

Example: ripples on a water surface

daydream
EDUCATIO

Amplitude

The maximum displacement of a point on a wave away from its undisturbed position

Frequency

The number of waves passing a particular point per second; measured in hertz (Hz):
1 Hz = 1 wave per second

Wavelength

The distance from a point on one wave to the equivalent point on an adjacent wave

Period

The time taken for a wave to complete a full cycle

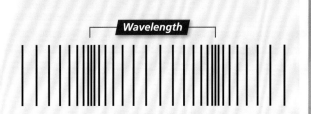

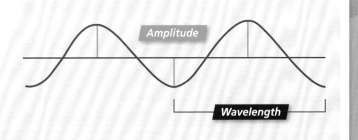

Period of a Wave

Use the equation below to calculate the period of a wave:

seconds (s)   hertz (Hz)

$$\text{period} = \frac{1}{\text{frequency}}$$

$$T = \frac{1}{f}$$

Example

The frequency of a wave is 50 Hz.

Calculate the period of the wave.

$$T = \frac{1}{f}$$

$$T = \frac{1}{50}$$

$$T = 0.02 \text{ s or } 20 \text{ ms}$$

Wave Speed

Wave speed is the speed at which energy is transferred, or the wave moves, through a medium. Use the equation below to calculate wave speed:

metres per second (m/s)   hertz (Hz)   metres (m)

$$\text{wave speed} = \text{frequency} \times \text{wavelength}$$
$$v = f\lambda$$

Example

A swimmer jumps into a pool, creating a wave. The wave travels at 4.9 m/s and has a wavelength of 40 cm. Calculate the frequency of the water waves.

$$v = f\lambda \leftarrow \text{Rearrange the equation to make } f \text{ the subject.}$$
$$f = \frac{v}{\lambda}$$
$$f = \frac{4.9}{0.4}$$
$$f = 12 \text{ Hz (2 s.f.)}$$

Investigate the suitability of apparatus to measure the frequency, wavelength and speed of waves in a ripple tank and waves in a solid.

Observing Water Waves in a Ripple Tank

In this activity, you will use a ripple tank to create waves. You can then measure the wavelength and frequency of the water waves to calculate the wave speed.

1 Set up the ripple tank as shown. Place a sheet of white card underneath so the waves can be clearly seen.

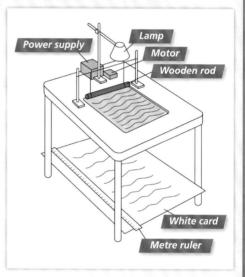

Power supply · Lamp · Motor · Wooden rod · White card · Metre ruler

2 Pour water into the tank to a depth of 5 mm, and adjust the rod so that it is just touching the water surface.

3 Switch on the electric motor and adjust its speed to produce low-frequency waves that can be counted.

4 Switch on the lamp and adjust its height so that the pattern of the waves can be clearly seen on the white card.

5 Place a metre ruler at a right angle to the waves shown on the card. Measure across as many waves as you can, and then divide that length by the number of waves to give the wavelength. Record this value in a table similar to the one on the next page.

6 Count the number of waves passing a chosen point in the pattern over a given time (e.g. 10 s). Then divide the number of counted waves by the given time period (e.g. 10 s) to find the frequency of the waves (number of waves per second).

7 Calculate the wave speed with the equation $v = f \lambda$ and record the values in the table.

Frequency (Hz)	Wavelength (m)	Speed (m/s)

daydream
EDUCATION

Observing Waves on a Stretched String or Elastic Cord

In this activity, you will use a vibration generator to create a stationary wave in a string. You can then measure the wavelength and frequency of the waves to calculate the wave speed.

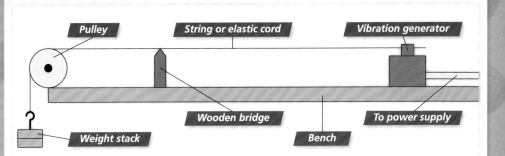

1 Set up the apparatus as shown, and switch on the vibration generator. The string will start to vibrate.

2 Adjust the tension in the string or move the wooden bridge to adjust the length of the string until you can see a clear stationary wave pattern.

3 Measure across as many loops (half wavelengths) as possible with a metre ruler. Then divide the total length by the number of loops. Multiply your answer by two to calculate the wavelength.

4 The frequency of the waves is equal to the frequency of the power supply.

5 Calculate the speed of the waves, and record this value in a table similar to the one below.

Frequency (Hz)	Wavelength (m)	Speed (m/s)

6 Repeat the steps above for different frequencies.

7 Review and compare the results from both practical activities. Consider how the apparatus used in both activities could be changed to improve the accuracy of the results.

Reflection & Refraction of Waves

Reflection

All waves can be reflected, absorbed or transmitted at a boundary between two different materials.

On diagrams, we draw the wave direction as a ray, a straight line with an arrowhead.

Normal – an imaginary line drawn at 90° to the boundary surface

Angle of incidence – the angle between the incident (incoming) ray and the normal

Angle of reflection – the angle between the reflected (outgoing) ray and the normal

Angle of incidence = Angle of reflection

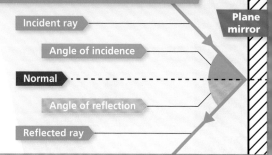

Plane mirror

Incident ray

Angle of incidence

Normal

Angle of reflection

Reflected ray

A Wave at a Boundary

When a wave arrives at a boundary, it can be:

1 **Absorbed by the second material on the far side of the boundary.** During absorption, energy is transferred to the energy store of the second material.

2 **Transmitted through the second material on the far side of the boundary.** The waves keep travelling through the second material but usually change speed. This can cause a change in direction of the wave, called refraction.

3 **Reflected at the boundary between the two materials.**

Specular Reflection

If a reflecting surface is smooth, waves are reflected in a single direction, like when light is reflected by a plane (flat) mirror. The angle of incidence is equal to the angle of reflection.

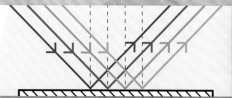

Diffuse Reflection

If a reflecting surface is rough, scattering occurs, which means waves are reflected in different directions.

Although the angle of incidence is equal to the angle of reflection, the normals are at different angles to each other. Thus, the waves are scattered.

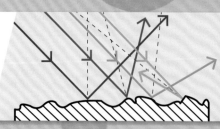

daydream
EDUCATION

Refraction

Refraction is the change of direction caused by the waves changing speed as they enter a different material. Depending on their wavelength, electromagnetic waves may be absorbed, transmitted, refracted or reflected by different substances.

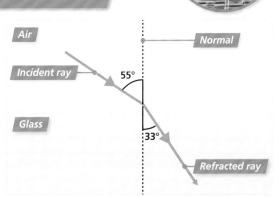

When waves travel from one medium to another, they change speed and usually direction. This is known as refraction.

A wave bends towards the normal when it slows down – that is, when it travels from a medium of lower optical density to one of higher optical density. Conversely, it bends away from the normal when it speeds up – that is, when it travels from a medium of higher optical density to one of lower optical density.

Air

Normal

Incident ray

55°

Glass

33°

Refracted ray

To remember this behaviour, use the acronym FAST:

Faster is **A**way. **S**lower is **T**owards.

The amount of refraction depends on the comparative optical densities of the two media: the greater the difference in optical density between the two media, the greater the degree of refraction.

Wave Front Diagram

When waves travel from one medium to another, their frequencies remain the same, but the wave speed changes. As a result, their wavelength changes.

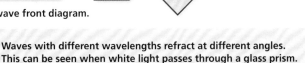

Wave speed = Frequency × Wavelength

This means that wave speed is proportional to wavelength.

Long wavelength

Short wavelength

Air

Long wavelength

Fast

Slow

Glass

Fast

This can be represented by a wave front diagram.

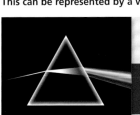

Waves with different wavelengths refract at different angles. This can be seen when white light passes through a glass prism.

The colours that make up white light have different wavelengths and are therefore refracted by different amounts, causing them to disperse (separate).

Investigate the reflection of light by different surfaces and the refraction of light by different substances.

1 With a ruler, draw a straight line near the middle of a piece of A3 paper. This represents the boundary surface.

2 Use a protractor to draw a second line at a right angle to the first line. Label this line N for normal.

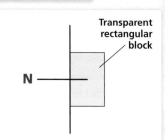

3 Place a transparent rectangular block on the paper. Line it up with the boundary surface line, and draw around it. (See the diagram opposite.)

4 Use a ray box or laser to shine a narrow ray of light at an angle onto the block where it meets the normal, as shown in the diagram below.

Warning: A ray box can get hot so be careful when you touch it. Switch it off when not in use.

5 Mark the paths of the incoming (incident) and outgoing (emergent and reflected) rays.

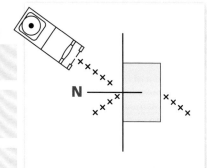

6 Remove the block, and join the incident and emergent rays with a straight line. This line represents the refracted ray.

7 Label the incident, reflected and refracted rays.

8 Use the protractor to measure the angle of incidence, angle of reflection and angle of refraction.

Record your measurements in a table like this one:

Block	Angle of Incidence	Angle of Reflection	Angle of Refraction

9 Repeat steps 1–8 with transparent blocks of different materials and record your results.

Theory suggests that the angles of incidence and reflection should be the same for a material, but the angle of refraction for that material will differ from (and be smaller than) the angle of incidence.

How well do your results support this theory for the two different materials that you tested?

daydream EDUCATION

Sound Waves

Sound waves are longitudinal waves produced when an object vibrates. The vibrations travel through different mediums (solids, liquids or gases) as a set of compressions and rarefactions. Particles of the medium vibrate parallel to the direction of the wave.

Compressions are regions of high pressure due to particles being close together.

Rarefactions are regions of low pressure due to particles being spread out.

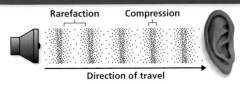

Rarefaction   Compression

Direction of travel

The speed of sound depends on the medium it is travelling through.

In general, sound waves travel slowest through gases, faster through liquids and fastest through solids. In solids, sound waves cause the particles to vibrate.

Medium	Speed of Sound Waves
Steel (solid)	5,800 m/s
Water (liquid)	1,000 m/s
Air (gas)	330 m/s

Sound cannot travel through a vacuum because there are no particles to carry the vibrations.

Hearing Sound

Within the ear, sound waves cause the eardrum and other parts to vibrate, which produces the sensation of sound.

Sound waves funnel through the pinna into the ear canal, where they cause the eardrum to vibrate.

Three small bones – the hammer, anvil and stirrup – transmit these vibrations to the cochlea.

The cochlea converts these vibrations into electrical signals. These signals then travel along the auditory nerve to the brain, which senses the sound.

The size and shape of our ear-drum limit the range of frequencies of sound that we can hear from 20 Hz to 20,000 Hz (20 kHz).

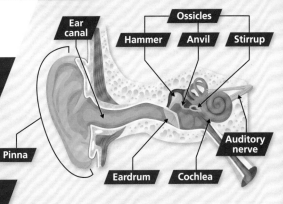

Ear canal

Ossicles

Hammer   Anvil   Stirrup

Auditory nerve

Pinna

Eardrum   Cochlea

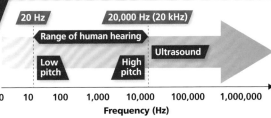

20 Hz

20,000 Hz (20 kHz)

Range of human hearing

Low pitch   High pitch

Ultrasound

| 0 | 10 | 100 | 1,000 | 10,000 | 100,000 | 1,000,000 |

Frequency (Hz)

Using Waves for Detection & Exploration

Variations in the velocity, absorption and reflection of different waves in solids and liquids means that they can be used for detection and exploration of hidden structures.

Ultrasound Waves

Ultrasound waves have a frequency that is higher than the upper limit of hearing for humans (20,000 Hz), and they are partially reflected when they meet a boundary between two materials.

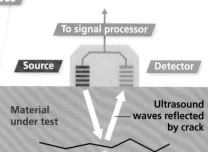

To signal processor

Source

Detector

Material under test

Ultrasound waves reflected by crack

The time it takes for reflections to reach a detector can be used to find the distance to a boundary.

In the example pictured, the depth of the boundary – the crack – can be calculated using the speed of sound in the material and the time it takes for the reflected wave to return.

Ultrasound waves are used for both medical and industrial imaging. In medical imaging, these waves are used to create images of internal parts of the body, enabling medical professionals to diagnose medical conditions and monitor unborn babies.

High-frequency sound waves are transmitted from a probe into the body.

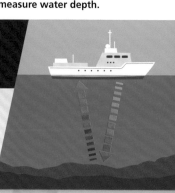

As the waves reach different organs and tissues (e.g. muscle and fat), they are partially reflected. Measuring these echo waves makes it possible to determine the location, size and shape of internal body parts.

The waves are instantly analysed by a computer and processed into an image.

Echo Sounding

In echo sounding, high-frequency sound waves, including ultrasound waves, are used to detect objects in deep water and to measure water depth.

A pulse of sound takes 3.2 s to travel from a ship to the seabed and back. The speed of sound in water is 1,500 m/s.

Calculate the depth of the ocean.

Distance = Speed × Time

Distance = 1,500 × 3.2 = 4,800 m

If this is the distance there and back, the depth of the ocean is:

4,800 ÷ 2 = 2,400 m or 2.4 km

daydream
EDUCATION

Seismic Waves

Seismic waves are produced by earthquakes in the Earth's crust.
These waves travel from the earthquake epicentre through the layers of the Earth.

Seismic waves can be detected by using seismometers on the Earth's surface.

By measuring the time it takes for seismic waves to reach seismometers and observing the pattern of where the waves are received, the make-up of the Earth's interior can be determined.

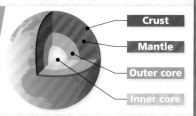

Crust

Mantle

Outer core

Inner core

Over time, the study of seismic waves has provided evidence about the hidden internal structure of the Earth.

There are two main types of seismic wave.

P-Waves

P-waves are longitudinal seismic waves. They travel through solids and liquids and are faster than S-waves.

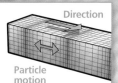

Direction

Particle motion

S-Waves

S-waves are transverse seismic waves. They cannot travel through liquids.

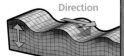

Direction

Particle motion

The speed of seismic waves depends on the density of the medium in which they travel. This makes it is possible to use the travel time of P-waves and S-waves through the Earth to identify its internal structure.

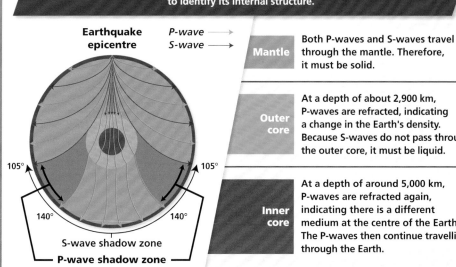

Earthquake epicentre

P-wave ⟶
S-wave ⟶

105°   105°
140°   140°

S-wave shadow zone
P-wave shadow zone

Mantle
Both P-waves and S-waves travel through the mantle. Therefore, it must be solid.

Outer core
At a depth of about 2,900 km, P-waves are refracted, indicating a change in the Earth's density. Because S-waves do not pass through the outer core, it must be liquid.

Inner core
At a depth of around 5,000 km, P-waves are refracted again, indicating there is a different medium at the centre of the Earth. The P-waves then continue travelling through the Earth.

daydream EDUCATION

Electromagnetic Waves

Electromagnetic (EM) waves are transverse waves that transfer energy from the wave source to an absorber. They form a continuous spectrum of different wavelengths but are grouped in order of their wavelength and their frequency.

EM waves travel at the same velocity (3×10^8 m/s) through a vacuum (such as space) or air.

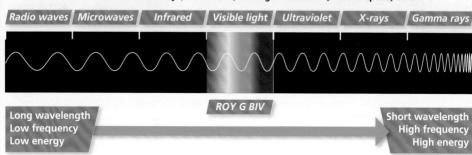

| Radio waves | Microwaves | Infrared | Visible light | Ultraviolet | X-rays | Gamma rays |

ROY G BIV

Long wavelength
Low frequency
Low energy

Short wavelength
High frequency
High energy

Our eyes can only detect visible light and, therefore, a limited range of EM waves.

Radio Waves

Radio waves are not made up of oscillating particles; they are made up of oscillating electric and magnetic fields. Therefore, they can be produced by oscillations in electrical circuits.

How Radio Waves Are Produced With Electricity

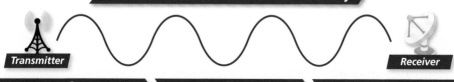

Transmitter

Receiver

1

A high-frequency alternating current (AC) is supplied to the transmitter, causing electrons in the antenna to oscillate.

2

The oscillating electrons produce oscillating magnetic fields (transverse (EM) radio waves), which have the same frequency as the AC.

3

When the waves reach the receiver, they are absorbed, causing electrons in the receiver to oscillate. This induces a current of the same frequency as the radio waves.

Changes in Atoms

Changes in atoms and their nuclei can result in EM waves being generated or absorbed over a wide frequency range, including gamma rays.

Gamma rays are produced by the disintegration of unstable (radioactive) nuclei and by the decay of certain particles. The nuclear energy store of the atom decreases when a gamma ray is emitted.

daydream
EDUCATIO

The Hazardous Effects of EM Waves

Some EM waves can have dangerous effects on human body tissue. These effects depend on the type of radiation and the size of the dose absorbed. The higher the frequency of the radiation, the higher its energy, so the more damage is likely to be caused.

Ultraviolet waves, X-rays and gamma rays all cause mutations to DNA which can lead to cancer. Ultraviolet waves (used in sunbeds) can cause skin to age prematurely and increase the risk of cancer. X-rays and gamma rays are ionising radiation that can also cause cancer.

The size of a radiation dose is a measure of the risk of harm resulting from the body's exposure to the radiation. It is measured in sieverts (Sv). 1000 millisieverts (mSv) = 1 sievert (Sv)

Type	Radio waves	Microwaves	Infrared (IR)	Visible light	Ultraviolet (UV)	X-rays	Gamma rays
Longer wavelength ⟵							⟶ Shorter wavelength
Lower frequency ⟵							⟶ Higher frequency
Dangers	Not thought to be hazardous	Heats water in the body; can kill cells	Felt as heat; can cause skin damage & burns	Can damage the eyes	Can cause sun burn, damage to eyes & cancer	Damages eyes and cells; causes cancer	Damages eyes and cells; causes cancer

Uses and Applications of EM Waves

Radio Waves

Radio waves are used to transmit television, radio and communication signals.

Long-wave radio signals can travel long distances because they diffract and follow the curvature of the Earth. Short-wave radio signals do not diffract, but they can travel long distances by reflecting off the part of the atmosphere called the ionosphere.

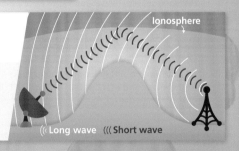

Microwaves

Microwaves are not strongly absorbed by the Earth's atmosphere, so they can be used to transmit signals to and from satellites.

The waves are sent by a transmitter to a receiver on a satellite orbiting the Earth. This satellite then transmits the waves back to Earth, where they are picked up by receivers.

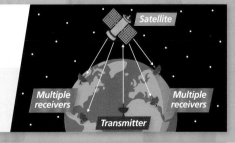

Water molecules in food absorb microwave radiation of certain wavelengths. This causes the water to heat up and cook the food. The water in living cells can also absorb microwave radiation, which can damage or kill living cells.

X-Rays & Gamma Rays

X-rays and gamma rays can penetrate our bodies.

X-rays are used in medical imaging. High-frequency X-rays are absorbed by dense body parts, such as bones, but pass through soft body tissues. This enables scanners to create negative images of internal body parts.

Gamma rays and high doses of X-rays can damage and kill living cells. Therefore, they can be used to kill cancer cells (radiotherapy).

Infrared Radiation (IR)

IR is used in electrical heaters, cookers, cameras and detectors.

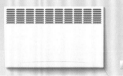

Visible Light

Visible light enables us to see. It is also used in fibre-optic communications, where data is coded into light pulses, which are sent along glass fibres.

Ultraviolet (UV)

Fluorescent objects absorb UV radiation and emit this energy as visible light.

In fluorescent lights, an electric current is used to excite a gas, causing it to emit UV light. A phosphor coating then absorbs the UV radiation and emits visible light.

Practical Activity:

Investigate how the amount of IR absorbed or radiated by a surface depends on the nature of that surface.

A Leslie cube is a hollow metal container that has different surfaces: shiny black, matt black, shiny silver and matt white. An infrared detector can be used to compare the amount of IR emitted from each surface.

1 Put the Leslie cube onto a heat-proof mat.

2 Fill the cube with very hot water, and put the lid on the cube.

3 Use the detector to measure the amount of IR emitted from each surface. Make sure that the detector is the same distance from each surface, and allow enough time between each reading for the detector to settle.

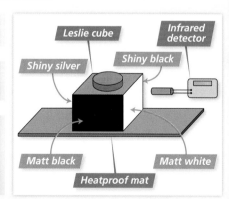

Leslie cube

Infrared detector

Shiny silver

Shiny black

Matt black

Matt white

Heatproof mat

Be careful when performing this experiment as you will be using very hot water.

daydream
EDUCATION

Lenses

A lens forms an image by changing the direction of, or refracting, light. When light passes from air into glass or plastic, it changes speed and usually direction because of the different densities of the materials. Lenses are used in cameras, microscopes and spectacles.

Convex and concave lenses have different shapes and opposite effects on light rays.

Convex Lenses

A **convex lens** is thicker at its centre than at its edges. It causes rays that are parallel to the principal axis to meet, or **converge**, at a point.

The point where the light rays meet is the principal focus.

Concave Lenses

A **concave lens** is thicker at its edges than at its centre. It causes rays that are parallel to the principal axis to spread out, or **diverge**.

The virtual point from which the light rays appear to diverge is the principal focus.

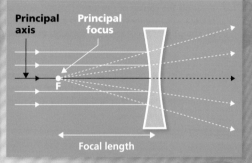

The distance from the centre of a lens to the principal focus is called the focal length. There is a principal focus on both sides of each lens.

A ray passing through the centre of a convex or concave lens continues in the same direction. It does not refract.

Real and Virtual Images

Real Images

A **real image** is produced when the light rays from an object converge at a specific point. This enables the image to be focused onto a screen.

The human eye produces a real image on the retina.

Real images can only be produced by a **convex lens** and appear **inverted** (upside down).

Virtual Images

A **virtual image** is produced when the light rays from an object appear to come from a certain point but actually come from somewhere else.

A mirror can also produce a virtual image, which appears to be behind the mirror.

Virtual images can be created by either **convex** or **concave** lenses and are generally **erect** (the right way up).

Ray Diagrams

Ray diagrams are used to determine the size, position and type of image formed by a lens. At least two rays are required to find this information.

Convex Lenses

To draw a ray diagram for an image (i) through a convex lens, follow the steps below.

1 Draw a ray (r1) from the top of the object (o) to the lens parallel to the principal axis. As the ray passes through the lens, it refracts. Draw the refracted ray so it goes through the principal focus.

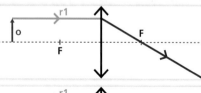

2 Draw a ray (r2) from the top of the object (o) through the centre of the lens. This ray does not refract so continue the ray in the same direction on the other side of the lens through the principal focus.

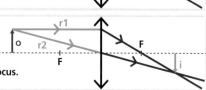

3 The top of the image (i) is found where the two rays cross. The bottom of the object is on the principal axis so you do not need to draw a ray to find the bottom of the image. The image produced is real and inverted (upside down).

Distance from the Convex Lens

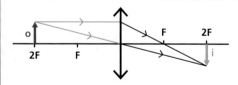

An object (o) at 2F creates a real, inverted image (i) that is the same size as the object and at 2F.

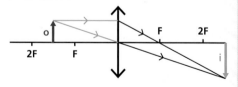

An object (o) between the principal focus (F) and 2F creates a real, inverted image (i) that is magnified and beyond 2F.

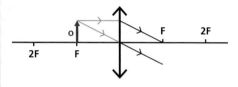

An object (o) at the principal focus (F) produces no image. The refracted rays are parallel so they neither converge nor diverge. Therefore, no image is produced.

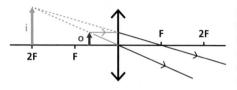

An object (o) nearer to the lens than the principal focus (F) produces a virtual image (i) that is erect, magnified and on the same side of the lens.

daydream
EDUCATION

Concave Lenses

The image produced by a concave lens is always virtual.

To draw a ray diagram for an image (i) through a concave lens, follow the steps below.

1 Draw a ray (r1) from the top of the object (o) to the lens parallel to the principal axis. Then draw a second ray (r2) from the top of the object to the centre of the lens.

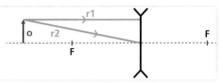

2 r1 is refracted so it appears to come from the principal focus. Therefore, draw a ray from the principal focus through the point where r1 hits the lens. r2 goes through the centre of the lens so it does not refract.

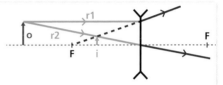

3 The top of the image (i) appears where the two rays cross. The bottom of the object (o) is on the principal axis, so there is no need to draw a ray to find the bottom of the image.

The image produced is always upright, smaller than the object (diminished) and virtual.

Magnification

The magnification produced by a lens is calculated with the following equation:

$$\text{magnification} = \frac{\text{image height}}{\text{object height}}$$

Magnification is a ratio so it has no units of measure. However, both the image height and object height should be measured in millimetres or centimetres.

An object that is 5 cm tall forms an image that is 32 cm tall. Calculate the magnification.

$$\text{magnification} = \frac{\text{image height}}{\text{object height}}$$

$$\text{magnification} = \frac{32}{5} = 6.4$$

Magnifying Glasses

A magnifying glass uses a convex lens to create a virtual image that is bigger than the object.

The object (o) must be closer to the lens than the principal focus. The image (i) produced is upright, magnified and virtual.

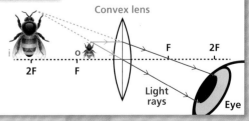

Visible Light

The visible light spectrum is the small part of the electromagnetic (EM) spectrum that we can see. Visible light is made up of a range of colours.

In the visible light spectrum, each colour has its own narrow band of wavelengths and frequencies These different frequencies of light are seen as different colours by the human eye. The colours can be mixed to make other colours, but the primary colours – pure red, pure green and pure blue – cannot be made by mixing other colours.

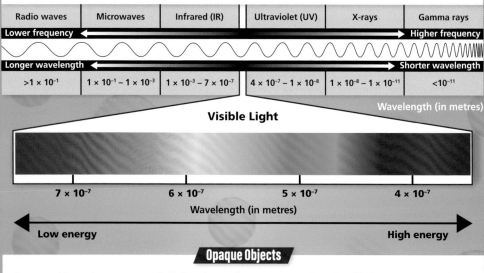

Radio waves	Microwaves	Infrared (IR)	Ultraviolet (UV)	X-rays	Gamma rays

Lower frequency ←————————————————————→ Higher frequency

Longer wavelength ←————————————————————→ Shorter wavelength

| $>1 \times 10^{-1}$ | $1 \times 10^{-1} - 1 \times 10^{-3}$ | $1 \times 10^{-3} - 7 \times 10^{-7}$ | $4 \times 10^{-7} - 1 \times 10^{-8}$ | $1 \times 10^{-8} - 1 \times 10^{-11}$ | $<10^{-11}$ |

Wavelength (in metres)

Visible Light

7×10^{-7} 6×10^{-7} 5×10^{-7} 4×10^{-7}

Wavelength (in metres)

Low energy ←————————————————————→ High energy

Opaque Objects

Opaque objects **do not transmit light**. They **reflect** some wavelengths of light but **absorb** others.

The reflection of light from a **smooth surface** in a single direction is called **specular reflection**. The reflection of light from a **rough surface** causes scattering, or **diffuse reflection**.

The colour of an opaque object is determined by the wavelengths of light that it most strongly reflects. Wavelengths that are not reflected are absorbed.

A green ball appears green because it most strongly reflects the wavelengths of light in the green range. The ball absorbs all other wavelengths.

If an object equally reflects all wavelengths, it appears white. If an object absorbs all wavelengths, it appears black.

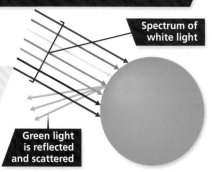

Spectrum of white light

Green light is reflected and scattered

Objects of non-primary colours may be reflecting that colour directly or a mixture of two primary colours. For example, a purple jumper may be reflecting only purple light, or it may be reflecting red and blue light.

daydream EDUCATION

Transparent & Translucent Objects

Transparent and translucent objects **transmit light**.

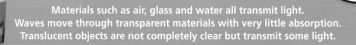

Materials such as air, glass and water all transmit light.
Waves move through transparent materials with very little absorption.
Translucent objects are not completely clear but transmit some light.

Colour Filters

Colour filters absorb certain wavelengths (colours) and transmit others.

A primary colour filter only lets that specific colour pass through. The other colours are absorbed.
A secondary colour filter lets the two primary colours that make the filter's colour pass through.

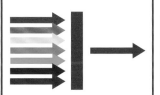

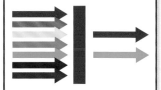

The red filter transmits only red wavelengths and absorbs all other colours.

The blue filter transmits only blue wavelengths and absorbs all other colours.

The magenta filter transmits blue and red wavelengths and absorbs all other colours.

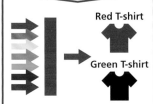

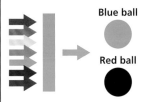

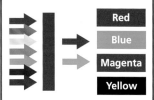

When a red filter is used, red objects still appear red. However, objects of all other colours appear black.

When a blue filter is used, blue objects still appear blue. However, objects of all other colours appear black.

When a magenta filter is used, red objects appear red, blue objects appear blue, and magenta objects appear magenta. All other colours appear black.

Black Body Radiation

All bodies (objects) can emit and absorb infrared radiation (IR) because of the energy in their thermal energy stores. The hotter the body, the more IR it emits in a given period.

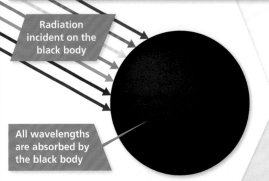

Radiation incident on the black body

A perfect black body absorbs all the radiation incident on it. It does not reflect or transmit any radiation.

All wavelengths are absorbed by the black body

Because a good absorber is also a good emitter, a perfect black body is the best possible emitter.

The intensity (power per unit area) and wavelength distribution of any emission from a body depends on the temperature of that body.

As a body gets hotter, the intensity of the radiation increases.

The intensity of shorter wavelengths increases faster than that of longer wavelengths.

As the body cools, the peak wavelength emitted has a longer wavelength but a lower intensity. This is shown on the graph below (λ max).

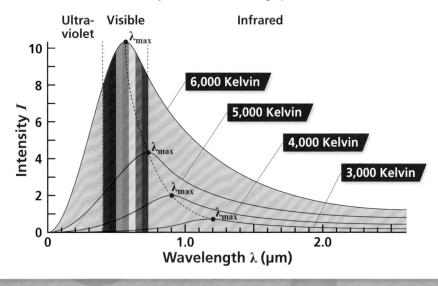

daydream
EDUCATION

Comparing emission and absorption helps explain the temperature of a body.

A body at constant temperature absorbs and emits radiation at the same rate.

The temperature of a body increases when the body absorbs radiation faster than it emits radiation.

Conversely, the temperature of a body decreases when the body absorbs radiation slower than it emits radiation.

Comparison	Temperature of Body
Emission > absorption	Decreasing
Emission = absorption	Constant
Emission < absorption	Increasing

Radiation Affects the Temperature of the Earth

The temperature of Earth depends on the rate at which radiation is absorbed and emitted by the Earth's surface and atmosphere and reflected into space.

The part of Earth facing the Sun absorbs lots of radiation, which causes an increase in temperature. Conversely, the part of Earth facing away from the Sun emits more radiation than it absorbs, causing a decrease in temperature.

Earth's overall temperature stays roughly constant.

However, human activities, such as burning fossil fuels, release carbon dioxide which increases radiation absorption in the atmosphere. As a result, Earth absorbs more radiation than it emits, causing the temperature to increase.

The Greenhouse Effect

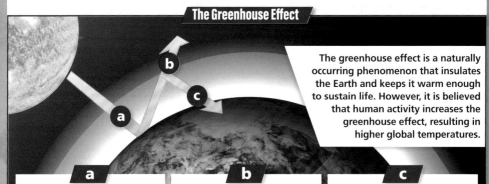

The greenhouse effect is a naturally occurring phenomenon that insulates the Earth and keeps it warm enough to sustain life. However, it is believed that human activity increases the greenhouse effect, resulting in higher global temperatures.

a
When the Sun's solar radiation reaches the Earth's surface, most of it is absorbed, but some is reflected into the atmosphere.

b
The Earth absorbs radiation with short wavelengths and warms up. Heat is then radiated from the Earth as longer wavelength infrared radiation.

c
Some of this infrared radiation is absorbed by greenhouse gases in the atmosphere, and the atmosphere warms up.

Magnetic Forces

Introduction

A magnet is a material or object that produces a magnetic field.
A magnetic force is a non-contact force exerted by magnets.
It is caused by the motion of electric charges.

All atoms in a substance contain negatively charged electrons that spin, generating an electric current. In most substances, equal numbers of electrons spin in opposite directions, cancelling out their magnetism. However, in magnetic substances such as iron, cobalt and nickel, the electrons spin in the same direction creating a magnetic field.

Magnetic Poles and Magnetic Fields

A magnet has two poles: a north-seeking pole and a south-seeking pole.

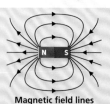

Magnetic field lines

The strength of a magnetic field depends on the distance from the magnet. It is strongest near the poles of the magnet.

Magnetic field lines are used to show a magnet's magnetic field. The closer together the lines are, the stronger the field. The direction of a magnetic field line is from the magnet's north-seeking pole to its south-seeking pole.

The magnetic field of a magnet can be seen by scattering iron filings around the magnet.

Attraction and Repulsion

When two magnets are placed close together, they exert a force on each other.

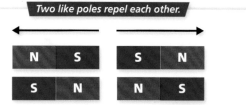

Two like poles repel each other.

| N | S | | S | N |

| S | N | | N | S |

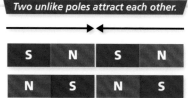

Two unlike poles attract each other.

| S | N | | S | N |

| N | S | | N | S |

Compasses

The Earth generates its own magnetic field. Therefore, a magnet (in the form of a compass) can be used to find the Earth's magnetic north and south and, consequently, for navigation and orientation.

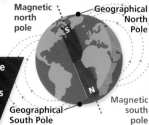

A compass contains a mounted magnetic bar that can spin freely. Because a magnet's poles are attracted to the Earth's magnetic poles, the two points of a compass will align with the Earth's magnetic field. The Earth's magnetic north pole attracts the north seeking ends of magnets, so it is technically the south pole of the Earth's magnetic field.

daydream
EDUCATION

A compass can also be used to determine the direction of the magnetic field around a magnet.

The north-seeking pole of a magnet always points towards the south pole of any nearby magnet. Therefore, you can move a compass around a magnet and trace its magnetic field and the direction of its magnetic force.

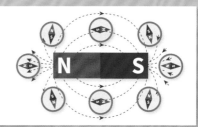

Permanent and Induced Magnets

A permanent magnet produces its own magnetic field. An induced magnet is a material that becomes magnetised when it is placed in a magnetic field.

Induced magnetism always causes a force of attraction. When removed from a magnetic field, an induced magnet loses most or all of its magnetism quickly. This can be demonstrated with a permanent magnet and two iron nails.

When you hold two iron nails together, they do not attract each other because neither is a permanent magnet.

When you place the iron nails next to a permanent magnet, they are attracted to it and become magnets themselves.

Once you remove the nails from the permanent magnet's magnetic field, they lose their magnetism.

1

2

3

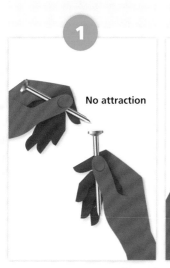

No attraction

Nails become induced and attract each other.

No attraction

Nail falls off

Electromagnetism

An electric current in a wire produces a magnetic field around the wire.

The strength of the magnetic field depends on the current through the wire and the distance from the wire. The greater the current, the stronger the magnetic field. The magnetic field is also stronger closer to the wire.

The direction of the magnetic field depends on the direction of the current and can be determined by using the right-hand thumb rule. If you point your right thumb in the direction of the current, your fingers will point in the direction of the magnetic field.

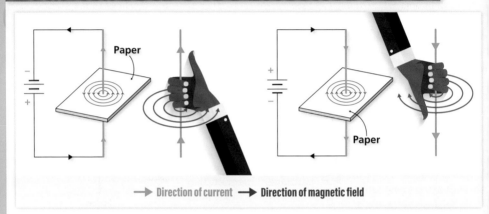

➡ Direction of current ➡ Direction of magnetic field

A long wire can be wrapped around a non-magnetic cylinder to make a solenoid. A solenoid increases the strength of a magnetic field created by a current through the wire.

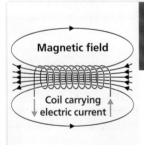

Magnetic field

Coil carrying electric current

Together, the magnetic field lines near each loop of wire result in lots of magnetic field lines pointing in the same direction. This makes the magnetic field inside a solenoid both strong and uniform.

The magnetic field lines have no start point or end point; they are loops. Inside the solenoid, the lines are (almost) parallel and close together, indicating a uniform and strong field. Outside the solenoid, the pattern is very similar to the magnetic field lines created by a bar magnet.

Adding an iron core to a solenoid increases the strength of its magnetic field and creates an electromagnet. However, as soon as the electric current is turned off, its magnetic field disappears.

daydream
EDUCATI

The Motor Effect

When a conductor (e.g. a wire) carrying a current is placed in a magnetic field, the magnet producing the field and the conductor exert a force on each other. This is called the motor effect.

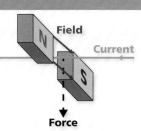

The force is greatest when the wire runs at a right angle to the magnetic field. When the wire runs parallel to the magnetic field, no force is exerted.

In the diagrams below, the invisible magnetic fields are represented by lines of magnetic flux. These lines show the effect, direction and strength of the magnetic field. When magnetic field lines are drawn close together, they show if the magnetic flux density is strong or high; lines drawn further apart show a weak or low magnetic flux density.

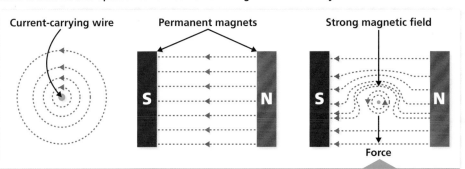

Current-carrying wire   Permanent magnets   Strong magnetic field

In the example above, you can see how the magnetic fields interact when they are at right angles to each other. The force that is produced on the wire is at right angles to the magnetic field and the direction of the current.

Fleming's left-hand rule can be used to find the direction of a force acting on a conductor in a magnetic field.

The size of the force acting on a conductor in a magnetic field depends on the strength of the magnetic field (magnetic flux density), the size of the current through the conductor and the length of the conductor.

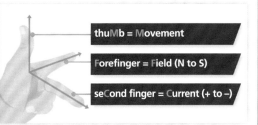

thuMb = Movement

Forefinger = Field (N to S)

seCond finger = Current (+ to –)

For a conductor at right angles to a magnetic field and carrying a current:

newtons (N)   tesla (T)   amperes or amps (A)   metres (m)

force = magnetic flux density × current × length

$$F = BIL$$

Electric Motors

A coil of wire carrying a current in a magnetic field will rotate. This is because the current is flowing in opposite directions in each side of the coil; one side experiences an upward force and the other a downward force. This is the basis of an electric motor.

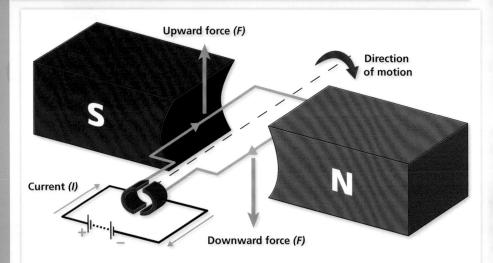

Upward force (F)

Direction of motion

S

N

Current (I)

Downward force (F)

If the direction of the current in the circuit is constant, the coil will not fully rotate. It will get to a vertical position and stop. Therefore, a commutator (a metal ring split into two halves) is used in motors to reverse the direction of the current in the coil every half turn.

In the context of the diagram, this means that the right-hand side always experiences a downward force and the left-hand side an upward force so the coil will fully rotate 360°.

To make the coil spin faster, you could:

- Supply a larger current (by using batteries with a higher potential difference).
- Increase the magnetic flux density (by using a stronger magnet or wrapping the coil onto an iron core).
- Increase the number of turns in the coil.

To make the coil spin in the opposite direction, you could reverse the magnets or the battery.

daydream

Loudspeakers

Loudspeakers and headphones (small loudspeakers) use the motor effect to convert variations in current in electrical circuits into air pressure variations in sound waves.

An **alternating current** passes through the **coil of wire**, which is attached to a paper cone. The **coil** becomes an electromagnet.

The **coil** (electromagnet) experiences a force from the permanent magnet, which makes the **coil**, and thus the cone, move.

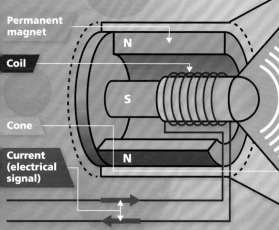

Permanent magnet

N

Coil

S

Cone

Current (electrical signal)

Cone vibrates

When the **current** is reversed, the force acts in the opposite direction and moves the cone the opposite way.

Changes in the **current** make the cone **vibrate** which causes the air molecules to move. This produces the pressure variations in the air which are needed to create a sound wave.

The frequency of the **current** controls the frequency of the vibrations that cause the sound. The amplitude of the **current** controls the size of the **vibrations** (loudness).

daydream
EDUCATION

Induced Potential

If an electrical conductor cuts through a magnetic field or a change occurs in the magnetic field around a conductor, a **potential difference** is induced across the ends of the conductor.

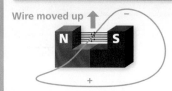

Wire moved up

If the conductor is part of a complete circuit, a current is induced in the conductor. This is called the **generator effect**.

An induced current generates a magnetic field that opposes the original change, either the movement of the conductor or the change in the magnetic field.

When a magnet is moved into a coil, it generates a current. When the magnet is removed from the coil, the current reverses. Therefore, moving the magnet in and out of the coil produces an alternating current.

The same effect can be achieved by reversing the polarity of the magnet.

Generators produce an alternating current by spinning a coil inside a magnetic field or rotating a magnet within a coil.

The size of the induced potential difference or current increases if:

- The speed of movement of the magnet or coil is increased
- The number of turns on the coil is increased
- The magnetic field strength is increased

Alternators

An alternator generates alternating current (AC) in a similar way to a motor.

Generators rotate a coil in a magnetic field to create a potential difference in the coil, which induces a current.

The current reverses direction in the coil every half turn, producing an alternating potential difference and current.

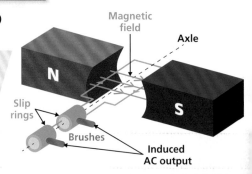

Magnetic field

Axle

Slip rings

Brushes

Induced AC output

Alternators have slip rings and brushes so the contacts do not swap every half turn and the coil remains free to move.

daydream
EDUCATI

Dynamos

A dynamo generates direct current (DC).

A dynamo works in a similar way to an alternator, but it has a split ring commutator in place of the slip rings.

The commutator swaps the connections to the brushes on every half turn, which keeps the current moving in the same direction.

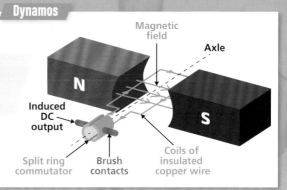

Magnetic field

Axle

N

S

Induced DC output

Split ring commutator

Brush contacts

Coils of insulated copper wire

Oscilloscopes

An oscilloscope is used to view the output from a generator. The potential difference (or voltage) is on the vertical axis, and time is on the horizontal axis.

The trace of the (AC) output from an alternator is an alternating sine curve that goes above and below the horizontal axis.

The trace of the (DC) output from a dynamo is not a straight line. It is a sine curve that is always above the horizontal axis but with the negative part flipped to positive.

The potential difference or current can be increased by:

- Increasing the number of turns on the coil
- Increasing the strength of the magnetic field
- Increasing the rate of rotation, which also increases the frequency of the trace

Microphones

Microphones use the generator effect to convert the air pressure variations in sound waves into variations in current in electrical circuits. This induces a potential difference in the coil initially, which leads to a current in the output circuit. They are loudspeakers working in reverse.

Sound waves hit the diaphragm, which makes the coil move in the magnet's field. This generates a current.

Louder sounds make the diaphragm move further, generating a larger current. A higher pitched sound will create a higher frequency electrical signal.

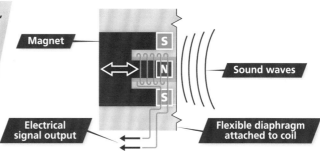

Magnet

S

N

S

Sound waves

Electrical signal output

Flexible diaphragm attached to coil

daydream
EDUCATION

Transformers

A transformer uses electromagnetic induction to change the potential difference (or voltage) of an alternating current (AC) supply. They are used in the National Grid (see National Grid page).

A basic transformer consists of a primary coil and a secondary coil wound around an iron core.

Iron is easily magnetised and increases the strength of the magnetic field.

1 An alternating potential difference is applied to the primary coil.

2 This produces a magnetic field, which changes as the current changes.

3 The changing magnetic field induces an alternating potential difference (or voltage) in the secondary coil.

This induced potential difference produces an AC in the circuit attached to the secondary coil (output).

A step-up transformer has fewer turns on the primary coil than the secondary coil. This means that the induced voltage across the secondary coil is greater than the applied voltage across the primary coil, increasing the potential difference or voltage.

A step-down transformer has more turns on the primary coil than the secondary coil. This means that the induced voltage across the secondary coil is less than the applied voltage across the primary coil, reducing the potential difference or voltage.

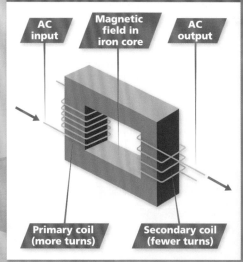

AC input	Magnetic field in iron core	AC output

Primary coil (fewer turns) Secondary coil (more turns)

Primary coil (more turns) Secondary coil (fewer turns)

daydream
EDUCATIO

The Transformer Equation

The ratio of the potential differences (voltages) across the primary (input) and secondary (output) coils of a transformer depends on the ratio of the number of turns on each coil.

$$\frac{V_p}{V_s} = \frac{N_p}{N_s}$$

The potential difference of the primary coil (V_p) and secondary coil (V_s) is measured in volts (V). N_p and N_s represent the number of turns on the primary coil and secondary coil, respectively.

In a step-up transformer $V_s > V_p$

In a step-down transformer $V_s < V_p$

A transformer has an input voltage of 100 V and an output voltage of 20 V.

$$N_s = \frac{N_p \times V_s}{V_p}$$

$$N_s = \frac{2,000 \times 20}{100}$$

If the primary coil has 2,000 turns, how many turns are in the secondary coil?

$$N_s = 400$$

A transformer is very efficient so is generally assumed to be 100% efficient. Therefore, electrical power output is assumed to be equal to electrical power input.

$$V_s \times I_s = V_p \times I_p$$

$V_s \times I_s$ determines the power output (secondary coil).
$V_p \times I_p$ determines the power input (primary coil).
Both are measured in watts (W).

A transformer has an input voltage of 240 V, an output voltage of 12 V and an output current (I_s) of 4 amps.

$$V_s \times I_s = 12 \times 4 = 48 \text{ W}$$

$$\text{If } V_s \times I_s = V_p \times I_p,$$

$$\text{then } V_p \times I_p = 48 \text{ W}$$

Calculate the output power and the input current.

$$I_p = \frac{48}{V_p} = \frac{48}{240} = 0.2 \text{ A}$$

Our Solar System

At the centre of our solar system there is a star called the Sun. Eight planets, plus dwarf planets, asteroids and comets orbit the sun. Natural satellites that orbit the planets, such as the Moon, are also part of our solar system.

A planet is a celestial body that:

 1 Orbits the Sun

 2 Has sufficient mass to assume a round shape and "clear the neighbourhood" around its orbit. This means that it has enough gravitational force to clear all objects in its orbit, other than its natural satellites.

Not to scale

Mars

Mercury

Saturn

Uranus

Earth

Pluto*

Venus

Jupiter

Neptune

* The discovery of Eris, which has 27% more mass than Pluto, led to Pluto's reclassification as a dwarf planet in 2006. Eris and three other celestial bodies were similarly classified.

Though these dwarf planets orbit the Sun and have sufficient mass to assume a round shape, they are not massive enough to clear all objects in their orbit.

Our solar system is a tiny part of the Milky Way galaxy, which is over 13 billion years old.

Our solar system is approximately 26,000 light years away from the supermassive black hole at the centre of the galaxy, which has about 4 million times more mass than the Sun.

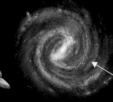

You are here

daydream EDUCATIO

Gravity Causes Objects to Move in Orbits

The planets orbit the Sun in an almost circular motion due to the gravitational pull of the Sun.
The Moon and artificial satellites orbit the Earth due to the gravitational pull of the Earth.

An object moving in a circle at a constant speed changes velocity (accelerates) because it constantly changes direction.

To keep a planet or satellite travelling in a circle (and accelerating), a resultant force is needed towards the centre.

For example, when the Moon orbits the Earth, the Earth's gravitational force acts as a centripetal force that pulls the Moon in, causing it to accelerate towards the centre of its orbit.

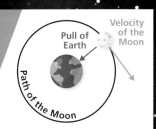

So why doesn't the Moon crash into the Earth?

The Moon has a velocity in the direction perpendicular to the force of the Earth's pull.
The centripetal force of Earth pulls in the Moon, causing it to orbit in an almost circular motion.
Without the pull of the Earth, the Moon would travel in a straight line.

The Relationship Between Orbital Speed and Distance from the Sun

The size (radius) of an orbit depends on an object's speed.

The size of the force of gravity between two objects increases as the distance between them decreases.

Therefore, an object in an orbit of small radius must move faster than an object in an orbit of large radius to stop it being pulled into the object it is orbiting.

Conversely, an object in an orbit of large radius must move slower than an object in an orbit of small radius to stop it flying off into space.

This can be seen clearly if we compare the orbital speed of the planets with their distances from the Sun.

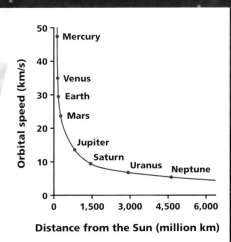

For an object to remain in a stable orbit, the radius of its orbit must change if its speed changes, and vice versa.

The Life Cycle of a Star

A star goes through a life cycle which is determined by its mass. It can be from 3 million years for the smallest stars to over 1,000 billion years for the most massive.

A star begins life when a **nebula**, a cloud of dust and gas, contracts due to gravitational forces. Gravity pulls matter in towards the centre of the cloud forming a **protostar**.

As more matter is pulled into the centre, the protostar gets denser, and its temperature increases.

The temperature continues to rise until it is hot enough for the nuclear fusion of hydrogen nuclei into helium nuclei, which releases lots of energy.

Forces inwards

Forces outwards

The force of gravity pulling matter into the centre of the protostar and the outward force caused by the fusion process eventually become equal.

This equilibrium means that the star becomes stable, so it neither contracts nor expands. The protostar now becomes a **main sequence star**.

This period of equilibrium can last billions of years, until the star runs out of hydrogen nuclei in its core. The Sun has been a main sequence star for about 4.6 billion years and will remain so for approximately another 5.4 billion years.

Stars About the Same Size as the Sun

When the hydrogen nuclei in the core begin to run out, the star expands into a **red giant**. It appears red because its surface has cooled. There is no longer enough energy to prevent the star from collapsing, so gravity starts to pull the star into itself.

Helium and other light elements in the core fuse, forming elements such as carbon. This process provides enough energy to stop the star from collapsing and, by pushing out the outermost layers of the star, actually enlarges it.

The star cools further and becomes unstable, shedding its outer layer of gas and dust. This leaves the hot, dense core as a **white dwarf star**.

Red giant

White dwarf

Black dwarf

As the white dwarf continues to cool, less energy is released, and eventually, the star becomes a **black dwarf**.

daydream EDUCATIO

Stars Much Bigger Than the Sun

When the hydrogen nuclei in the core begin to run out, the star expands into a **red super giant**. Fusion continues and the star begins to glow more brightly. The star expands and contracts several times, forming heavy elements such as iron.

Eventually, the massive star explodes. Without the outward force from nuclear fusion, there is nothing to counteract the inward force of gravity. Therefore, the core becomes so dense that it collapses under the force of gravity, resulting in the giant explosion of a supernova.

After the explosion, naturally occurring elements that are heavier than iron form and are distributed throughout the universe. The core remains a very dense neutron star, while the star dust forms new protostars.

If the star is massive enough, a black hole will form. A black hole has a gravitational field so intense that no matter, including light, can escape from it.

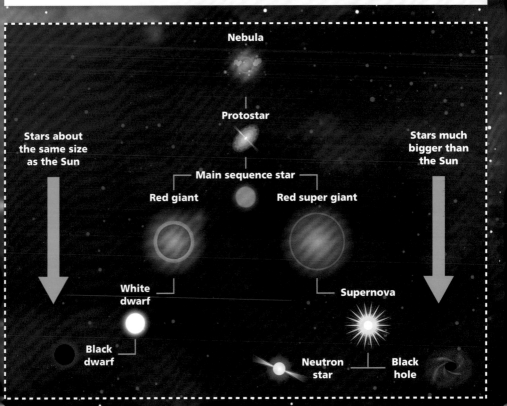

Nebula

Protostar

Stars about the same size as the Sun

Stars much bigger than the Sun

Main sequence star

Red giant

Red super giant

White dwarf

Supernova

Black dwarf

Neutron star

Black hole

Red-Shift

Red-shift is a phenomenon that provides evidence that the universe is expanding.

Source moving away from a point

Direction of movement

Source moving towards a point

Increased wavelength

Decreased frequency

Decreased wavelength

Increased frequency

If the source of waves (s) is moving away from a point, it emits each wave from a position that is farther from the point than the previous wave.

As a result, the arrival time between successive waves becomes longer, increasing the wavelength **and decreasing the frequency.**

If the source of waves (s) is moving towards a point, it emits each wave from a position that is closer to the point than the previous wave.

As a result, the arrival time between successive waves becomes shorter, decreasing the wavelength **and** increasing the frequency.

When the spectrum of light from distant galaxies is observed from Earth it looks different to the spectrum of light from the Sun. The spectrum has moved (shifted) towards the red end of the spectrum as the wavelengths have increased.

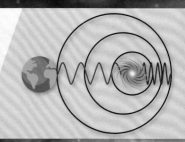

The further away the galaxies are, the faster they move and the bigger the observed increase in wavelength. This phenomenon is called **red-shift**.

The observed red-shift provides evidence that the source of light and space itself (the universe) are expanding. The spectral diagrams below show how the movement of an object affects its line spectrum.

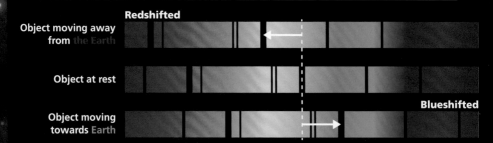

Redshifted

Object moving away from the Earth

Object at rest

Blueshifted

Object moving towards Earth

If distant galaxies were getting closer, the spectrum of light would shift towards the blue end of the visible spectrum as wavelengths decreased. This phenomenon is called blue shift.

daydream EDUCATIO

The Big Bang

Evidence from red-shift indicates that the universe is expanding in all directions, and it supports the Big Bang theory – the idea that the universe started with a big expansion of space from a very small point.

Scientists have also discovered cosmic microwave background radiation (CMBR), which is believed to be the energy left over from the Big Bang, now spread over the entire universe.

Future Ideas

It is still unknown whether our universe will expand forever or whether the force of gravity among the universe's contents will eventually pull the universe back together in a 'Big Crunch'.

Dark Energy and Dark Matter

Distant galaxies are moving away from Earth at a faster rate than closer galaxies, and the expansion of the universe seems to be accelerating. However, the reasons for this are unknown.

One suggested theory is dark matter and the expansive force of dark energy.

Very little is known about dark energy and dark matter, but they are thought to make up around 95% of the universe (dark matter, 27%; dark energy, 68%).

Dark energy is believed to be the invisible force that is making the universe expand.

According to scientific data, galaxies are rotating too quickly given the **observed** mass of their stars. This suggests that there must be some other mass in the universe: dark matter.

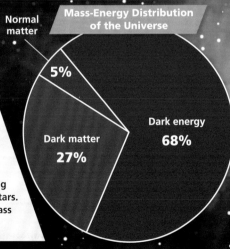

Mass-Energy Distribution of the Universe

Normal matter 5%

Dark matter 27%

Dark energy 68%

Because of their names, it is easy to confuse dark matter and dark energy. Although they may be related, their effects are quite different. In brief, dark matter attracts, and dark energy repels. Lots of new theories about dark energy and dark matter are being put forward. These will get tested by other scientists and may be rejected or accepted, possibly with some modification.

daydream
EDUCATION

Applications of Science

Scientific developments have led to remarkable discoveries and innovations. However, they have also created issues related to social, economic, environmental and ethical factors. Therefore, the evaluation of scientific applications should consider the advantages and disadvantages related to these issues.

Example: Evaluate the use of zoos to breed animals.

When evaluating something, always remember to consider the arguments for and against.

Social

How do zoos affect people?

- Zoos stimulate interest in animals and provide an opportunity to educate people and to promote animal protection.
- Animals can escape.

Economic

How do zoos affect the economy?

- Zoos create jobs and support local businesses.
- Some zoos donate money to animal charities.
- Zoos can be expensive to run and maintain.

Environmental

How do zoos affect the environment?

- Zoos provide a home for animals that have had their habitats destroyed.
- Removing animals from the wild can further endanger the wild population.

Ethical

Are zoos ethical?

- Zoos save endangered species and can help breed endangered species.
- It is cruel to keep animals in captivity.
- Surplus animals are sometimes killed.

Personal: How do zoos affect you?   Do zoos affect your life in a positive or negative way?

 It is not always possible to answer questions relating to scientific developments, especially ethical questions. This is particularly difficult when there is little or no existing data. Sometimes it can take years of research for new data to come to light.

For example, for years, diesel was promoted as a way of reducing CO_2 emissions. However, in 2012, studies by the European Environment Agency found evidence that nitrogen dioxide (NO2) from diesel fumes were very harmful to human health, causing thousands of premature deaths each year. As a result, there has been a push to phase out diesel cars.

Peer Review

Peer review is a process that involves the evaluation of scientific, academic or professional work by others working in the same field.

Scientists publish their results in scientific journals. Before a work is published, its validity is checked by experts – this is peer review.

Scientific journals are print and online magazines that contain articles written by scientists about their research.

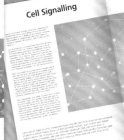

Publication can lead to collaborations between scientists to develop ideas or inspire new ones.

It is important that experts review research in journals. Peer review lets readers know that they can be confident that the claims made are valid and believable. However, this does not mean the research findings are correct, just that they are not obviously wrong.

The Peer Review Process

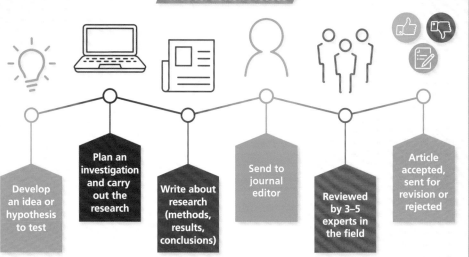

Develop an idea or hypothesis to test

Plan an investigation and carry out the research

Write about research (methods, results, conclusions)

Send to journal editor

Reviewed by 3–5 experts in the field

Article accepted, sent for revision or rejected

Beware!

Scientific reports in the media do not go through peer review so they may be inaccurate or biased. If the report is based on a journal article, get more reliable information by reading the conclusions of the research.

Risk

*A **hazard** is anything that can cause harm.*
Risk is the likelihood of a hazard causing harm.

Measuring Risk

The size of risk posed by something depends on how hazardous (harmful) it is and the likelihood of it happening. Look at the example below:

Lightning is **very hazardous** – it can kill.
But the **likelihood** of being hit by lightning is **very low**.
Therefore, the risk of being killed by lightning is low.

Hazards & Risk in Science

There are various hazards in practical science. It is important to identify these hazards and to try to reduce their risk and the likelihood of them occurring and causing harm.

Although scientific or technological developments frequently bring about many benefits, they can also often introduce new risks.

For example, the development of e-cigarettes has helped significantly increase the number of people giving up smoking. However, scientists are still unsure whether the chemicals used in the cigarettes are harmful to the body.

Look at the two examples below. Are the benefits of these technologies worth the risk?

Genetic Engineering

➕ **Benefit:** Genetic engineering can significantly increase food production.

➖ **Risk:** There are serious concerns about the effects of genetically modified foods on human health and biodiversity. Also, gene transfer between plants may lead to an uncontrollable 'escape' of genes into wild plants.

X-Rays

➕ **Benefit:** X-rays are used to check for bone fractures.

➖ **Risk:** Radiation exposure can cause cell mutations that may lead to cancer. However, this risk is thought to be very low.

daydrea

The size of risk posed by a hazard can be measured by looking at the number of times the hazard caused harm in a sample. Look at the example below:

Deaths per 1 billion passenger miles

Motorcycle	212.57
Car	7.28

The statistics above show that travelling by motorcycle is riskier than travelling by car.

Perceived Risk vs Measured Risk

The perception of risk is often very different from measured risk.

Familiar vs Unfamiliar

Which has the higher risk?

Running a marathon

or

Parachuting out of a plane

Although most people think parachuting out of a plane is riskier than running a marathon, the risk of dying in both activities is roughly the same: eight in one million. This is because familiar things feel less risky than unfamiliar things.

Visible vs Invisible

Some 3.8 million premature deaths are annually attributed to air pollution. However, because air pollution is invisible, people tend to underestimate its risk. This is the same for many other invisible hazards.

A similar perception applies to hazards that take a long time to take effect, such as an unhealthy diet.

Imposed vs Voluntary

Around 200 years ago, the leading cause of death was communicable diseases caused by poor sanitation and living conditions. People usually did not have a choice about this – the risks were imposed.

Now, the leading cause of death is non-communicable diseases like heart disease and cancer. Often, the risk of these is increased by lifestyle choices, or voluntary risks.

In general, people are more likely to accept the risks that are within their control than the risks over which they have no control.

Apparatus

Scientific apparatus are specialist instruments that are used during experiments. During experiments, it is important to use the correct apparatus, wear the appropriate protective equipment and understand the hazards involved.

Experimental Apparatus

Bunsen Burner	Conical Flask	Filter Paper & Funnel	Test Tubes	Clamp Stand
A heating apparatus used in laboratories	Used for heating and collecting solutions	Used for separating solids from liquids	Used for heating and testing small quantities of solids and liquids	Used to safely hold apparatus in position

Spatula	Tripod & Gauze	Beaker	Evaporating Dish
Used to handle solids and transfer them from containers	Used to support apparatus above a Bunsen burner	Used for stirring, mixing and heating liquids	Used to heat and evaporate liquids

Measuring Apparatus

Measuring Cylinder	Stopwatch	Newtonmeter/ Forcemeter	Thermometer
Volume – cm³, dm³, ml, l	Time – s, min	Force – N	Temperature – °C

daydream
EDUCATIO

Hazards

A hazard is something that poses a risk and that could potentially cause harm. Hazard symbols are used on containers to indicate the dangers associated with the contents and to inform people about how to use the substance safely.

 Explosive   **Flammable**   **Oxidising**   **Corrosive**   **Toxic**   **Health hazard**

Safety

Hairnet or Hair Tie

Holds or ties hair back out of the way

Lab Coat

Protects skin and clothes from harmful substances

Safety Glasses

Used at all times to protect the eyes

Risk Assessment

Risk Assessment

When planning an experiment, complete a risk assessment to identify the hazards, associated risks and the ways in which they can be reduced. It is important to assess the likelihood of something going wrong and the seriousness of the consequences if it does go wrong.

Safety Gloves

Used when handling hot or harmful materials

Physical Units

International System of Units (SI Units)

Quantity Name	Unit Name	Unit Symbol
Length	metre	m
Mass	kilogram	kg
Time	second	s
Electric current	ampere	A
Thermodynamic temperature	kelvin	K
Amount of substance	mole	mol
Luminous intensity	candela	cd

Other Units

Quantity Name	Unit Name	Unit Symbol
Temperature	degree Celsius	°C
Energy	joule	J
Frequency	hertz	Hz
Force or weight	newton	N
Pressure	pascal	Pa
Power	watt	W
Voltage (potential difference)	volt	V
Resistance	ohm	Ω
Charge	coulomb	C
Capacitance	farad	F

SI Prefixes

These are added to unit names to produce multiples and sub-multiples, or fractions, of the original unit.

Multiples

Factor	Name	Symbol
10^{12}	tera	T
10^9	giga	G
10^6	mega	M
10^3	kilo	k
10^2	hecto	h
10^1	deca	da

Fractions

Factor	Name	Symbol
10^{-12}	pico	p
10^{-9}	nano	n
10^{-6}	micro	μ
10^{-3}	milli	m
10^{-2}	centi	c
10^{-1}	deci	d

Examples

You need to be able to convert from one unit to another.

10^3 m (1,000 m) = 1 km 10^3 g (1,000 g) = 1 kg 10^{-2} m (0.01 m) = 1 cm 10^{-3} g (0.001 g) = 1 mg

Planning

A good plan is well designed for its purpose.

Reasons to Plan an Investigation

Make Observations

What structures can be seen in cells?

Produce a Substance

How can a salt be made using neutralisation?

Test a Hypothesis

Is the extension of a spring proportional to the weight added?

Explore Phenomenon

What are wave patterns like in oceans across the world?

What to Think About When Planning

What data or observations need to be collected?
- How many measurements need to be taken to see a pattern?
- What range of measurements is needed?
- How many repeats is enough?

- I need to measure the extension of the spring as the mass on the end changes.
- I will increase the mass by 10 g (0.1 N) until 100 g (1 N) is reached. I will repeat the experiment twice.

What apparatus and techniques should be used?

- I will use a spring held on a clamp stand, a 50-cm ruler and slotted masses.
- I will measure extension by viewing the spring at eye level and taking the reading from the bottom of the spring.

How is the apparatus used to record accurate measurements?

- I will attach the ruler to the clamp stand to make sure it is measuring the length of the spring accurately.

What are the possible hazards? How can the risk of harm be reduced?

- The clamp stand could fall over. Therefore, I will attach the clamp stand to the table with a clamp and make sure it is not placed over my feet.

What are the variables?

- Independent variable = mass
- Dependent variable = length of extension

Variables

Investigations are often performed to identify if there are patterns or relationships between two variables. One variable is changed to see how it affects another variable.

Independent Variable
The independent variable is the one that is changed.

Dependent Variable
The dependent variable is the one that is measured for each change in the independent variable; it's what the investigator thinks will be affected during the experiment.

Control Variables
Control variables are all the other variables in an investigation that should be kept the same to ensure that it is the independent variable that is causing the dependent variable to change.

Presenting Data

Presenting data in an appropriate way makes it easy to spot patterns and draw conclusions from results.

Categorical Data

Includes non-numerical data (e.g. colour) and numerical data with definite values (e.g. number of cells)

Continuous Data

Numerical data that can take any value (e.g. height or time)

A population of plants is found growing in a field, including in a shady area under a tree.

There is lots of data that can be measured to answer the question:

How do light and shade affect plant growth?

Graphing Rules

- Label both axes.
- Give your charts and graphs a title.
- Include a key if you have more than one set of data.
- Usually, the dependent variable goes on the y-axis and the independent variable on the x-axis.

Bar Charts

Bar charts are used to present categorical data. Bar charts help to compare data.

Leave a gap between each bar.

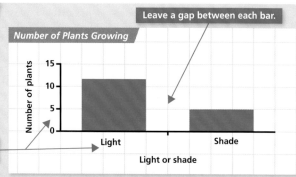

Number of Plants Growing

Number of plants: 15, 10, 5, 0

Light   Shade

Light or shade

Use equal intervals on both axes.

daydream
EDUCATION

Line Graph

Line graphs are used to display continuous data. They can be used to show trends and change over time.

Change over Time

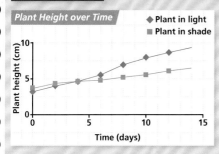

Plant Height over Time
◆ Plant in light
■ Plant in shade

Data is plotted as a series of points that are joined by straight lines.

A Trend

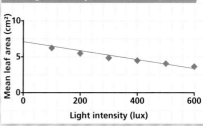

How Light Intensity Affects Mean Leaf Area

A line of best fit can be drawn to show an overall trend and that a proportional relationship exists between the two variables. In this example, as light intensity increases, mean leaf area decreases.

Frequency Tables and Charts

A frequency table is used to record how often a value (or set of values) occurs.

Length of Top Leaf (cm)	Frequency	
	Plants in Shade	Plants in Light
$3.0 \leq l < 3.5$	2	3
$3.5 \leq l < 4.0$	5	7
$4.0 \leq l < 4.5$	4	5
$4.5 \leq l < 5.0$	7	6
$5.0 \leq l < 5.5$	7	4
Total	**25**	**25**

Data from frequency tables is often displayed in frequency charts.

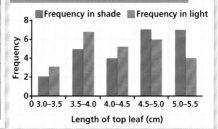

How Light Intensity Affects Leaf Length
■ Frequency in shade ■ Frequency in light

The groups (intervals) must be the same. Make sure to include units of measure in the column headings. A sample of 25 plants from each environment was used. The interval $5.0 \leq l < 5.5$ is equal to or greater than 5.0 and less than 5.5.

Evaluating Data

Students performed an experiment to determine how temperature affects reaction rate. They measured the time taken for a certain amount of sulfur to form when sodium thiosulfate solution reacts with acid at different temperatures.

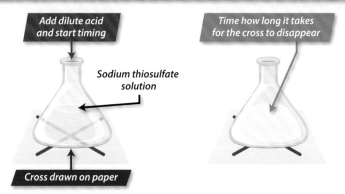

Add dilute acid and start timing

Time how long it takes for the cross to disappear

Sodium thiosulfate solution

Cross drawn on paper

This was measured by determining how long it took for the solution to become completely opaque at different temperatures.

Temperature (°C)	Time for Cross to Disappear (s)		
	1	2	3
10	196	194	196
20	95	88	96
30	53	53	53
40	28	24	26

Precision

Measurements are precise if they are similar and cluster around a single value.

How to Check for Precision: Look how close the repeated values are.

Evaluation: At 30°C, the repeats are all the same, which means these results are very precise. The results at 40°C are not as precise because they have a range of 4 seconds.

Range: the difference between the lowest and highest measurements

daydream EDUCATION

Accuracy

An accurate measurement is one that is close to the true value. There are few errors and little uncertainty.

How to Check for Accuracy:

Errors: Random errors are shown by anomalous (odd-looking) results, but they can be reduced by taking more measurements and finding the mean value.

Systematic errors are difficult to spot from results, so the equipment should be checked. Any anomalies should be investigated to try and find the cause and, if due to error, should be discarded.

Random error: results varying in unpredictable ways

Systematic error: measurements that differ from the true value by a consistent amount every time; usually caused by a problem with the measuring equipment

Mean

The sum of values divided by the number of values

Example for 40°C: $\dfrac{28 + 24 + 26}{3} = 26$

Percentage Uncertainty

$$\dfrac{\text{range}}{\text{mean}} \times 100$$

Example for 40°C: $\dfrac{4}{26} \times 100 = 15.38$

Uncertainty: The range of measurements around the mean. A low uncertainty is a sign of high accuracy.

Evaluation: The second recorded value at 20°C (88 s) is an anomaly (probably due to a mistake in measurement). The uncertainty is highest for 40°C because these show the most variation around the mean.

Repeatability

Measurements are considered repeatable if they produce similar results when performed by the same investigator under the same conditions.

How to Check for Repeatability:
Look how close the repeats are.
In the experiment above, the measurements show good repeatability because the overall measurements are around the same for each repeated value.

Reproducibility

Measurements are considered reproducible if they produce similar results when performed by a different investigator with different equipment.

How to Check for Reproducibility:
Get someone else to carry out the experiment using different equipment. If their experiment produces similar results to yours, the measurements can be considered reproducible.

daydream
EDUCATION

Standard Form

Standard form, or standard index form, is used when writing very small or very large numbers.

In standard form, a number is always written in the following format:

A is always a number between 1 and 10:
$1 \leq A < 10$

$$A \times 10^n$$

n tells you how many places you need to move the decimal point.

Converting Numbers into Standard Form

When writing large numbers in standard form, n is always positive.						
8,000,000	=	$8 \times 1,000,000$	=	8×10^6
45,000,000	=	$4.5 \times 10,000,000$	=	4.5×10^7
160,000	=	$1.6 \times 100,000$	=	1.6×10^5

When writing small numbers in standard form, n is always negative.				
0.000465	=	$4.65 \div 10,000$	=	4.65×10^{-4}
0.009	=	$9 \div 1,000$	=	9.0×10^{-3}
0.0000077	=	$7.7 \div 1,000,000$	=	7.7×10^{-6}

Examples

Example 1

There are around 87,000,000 species on the Earth. Convert this to standard form.

$$87,000,000 = 8.7 \times 10,000,000 = 8.7 \times 10^7$$

The decimal point has moved seven places to the left:

8.7000000

7 6 5 4 3 2 1

Example 2

The diameter of the DNA helix is 0.000000002 m. Convert this to standard form.

$$0.000000002 = 2.0 \div 1,000,000,000 = 2 \times 10^{-9}$$

The decimal point has moved nine places to the right:

0000000002.0

1 2 3 4 5 6 7 8 9

daydream EDUCATION

Rounding to Significant Figures

Significant Figures

If something is 'significant', it is large or important.
Therefore, 'most significant' means 'largest' or 'most important'.

In the number 169.2, the most significant figure is 1 because it has the largest value, 100.	Hundreds	Tens	Ones		Tenths
	1	6	9	•	2

The first significant figure in a number is the first digit that is not zero. Any leading zeros are insignificant (placeholders).	0302.14 00.507 0.00621

Rounding to Significant Figures

To round to significant figures, identify the significant figure that is being rounded to and round as normal.

The density of iron is 7.874 g/cm³. To round 7.874 to 2 significant figures:

1	Identify the second significant figure.	7.874
2	Look at the digit to the right of the one that is being rounded. It is more than 5 so round up.	7.874
3	When rounding decimals, there is no need to add zeros after the significant figures.	7.9

7.874 rounded to 2 significant figures is 7.9.

An object has a mass of 0.046748 g. To round 0.046748 to 3 significant figures:

1	Identify the third significant figure.	0.046748
2	Look at the digit to the right of the one that is being rounded. It is less than 5 so leave it alone.	0.046748
3	When rounding decimals, there is no need to add zeros after the significant figures.	0.0467

0.046748 rounded to 3 significant figures is 0.0467.

Taylor ran 400 metres in 52 seconds. Calculate her speed to 2 significant figures.

1	Calculate Taylor's speed: speed = $\frac{\text{distance}}{\text{time}}$ = $\frac{400}{52}$ = 7.692307692 m/s	
2	Identify the second significant figure.	7.692307692
3	Look at the digit to the right of the one that is being rounded. It is more than 5 so round up.	7.692307692
4	When rounding decimals, there is no need to add zeros after the significant figures.	7.7

Taylor's speed to 2 significant figures was 7.7 m/s.

Averages

An average is a measure of the middle value of a data set. There are three main types of averages: mean, mode and median.

Mean

The mean is the sum of the values divided by the number of values.

$$\text{mean} = \frac{\text{sum of values}}{\text{number of values}}$$

Abbie is measuring her reaction time using the ruler drop test:

Attempt	1	2	3	4	5	6	7	8	9	10
Distance (cm)	19.5	18	12	16	12	10.6	7.5	8	6.4	7

$$\text{Mean} = \frac{19.5 + 18 + 12 + 16 + 12 + 10.6 + 7.5 + 8 + 6.4 + 7}{10} = \frac{117}{10} = 11.7 \text{ cm}$$

Mode

The mode is the value that occurs most often.

The mode for Abbie's results was 12 cm.
It occurred twice, in her third and fifth attempts.

Median

The median is the middle value when the data is arranged in order of size.

Attempt	9	10	7	8	6	3	5	4	2	1
Distance (cm)	6.4	7	7.5	8	10.6	12	12	16	18	19.5

As there is an even number of values, the median is the mean of the middle two values.

$$\text{Median} = \frac{10.6 + 12}{2} = \frac{22.6}{2} = 11.3 \text{ cm}$$

Range

The range is the difference between the lowest value and the highest value in a data set.

| Attempt 9 6.4 | ← Range = 13.1 → | Attempt 1 19.5 |

To find the range, subtract the lowest value from the highest value.
The range of Abbie's results is 13.1 cm.

daydream EDUCATION

Scatter Graphs

Scatter graphs are used to show how closely two sets of data are related. Correlation describes how the two sets of data are related.

Positive Correlation

When the **plotted points** go upward from left to right, there is **positive correlation**.

As one quantity increases, the other increases. As one quantity decreases, the other decreases.

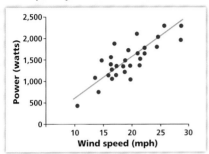

This graph shows that there is positive correlation between wind speed and the amount of electricity generated by a wind turbine. As the speed of a wind turbine increases, so does the amount of electricity generated.

Negative Correlation

When the **plotted points** go downward from left to right, there is negative correlation.

As one quantity increases, the other decreases.

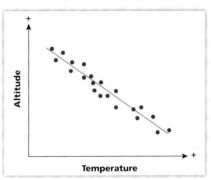

This graph shows that there is negative correlation between altitude and temperature. As altitude increases, temperature decreases.

No Correlation

When there is no linear relationship between two data sets, there is no correlation.

This graph shows that the number of children that a person has is not related to his/her average daily sugar consumption.

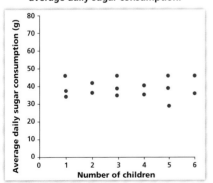

Line of Best Fit

A line of best fit is a line that is drawn through the centre of a group of data points.

When the plotted points are close to the line of best fit, there is **strong correlation**. When they are spread out on either side of the line of best fit, there is **moderate correlation**.

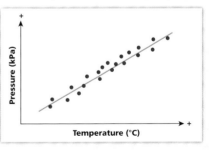

This graph shows a **strong positive correlation**.

Correlation and Causation

A correlation between two variables does not necessarily mean there is a direct cause-and-effect relationship between them.

Example >>> There is a strong positive correlation between germ exposure and disease development. However, these variables are not directly related. Germs alone do not cause disease. The causative factor is a compromised immune system.

Rearranging Formulae

Sometimes you can rearrange formulae by using inverse operations to make them easier to work with and solve. In the examples below, the equations have been rearranged to make x the subject:

$x - 4 = 9$
$+4 \qquad +4$
$x = 13$

Addition and **subtraction** are inverse operations.

$x + 7 = 12$
$-7 \qquad -7$
$x = 5$

$mx = t$
$\div m \qquad \div m$
$x = \dfrac{t}{m}$

Multiplication and **division** are inverse operations.

$\dfrac{x}{r} = 12$
$\times r \qquad \times r$
$x = 12r$

$x^2 = w$
$\sqrt{} \qquad \sqrt{}$
$x = \pm\sqrt{w}$

Finding the **square root** of a number is the inverse operation of **squaring** that number.

Square
$\sqrt{x} = a$
$2 \qquad 2$
$x = a^2$

You can rearrange the formula for speed to make distance or time the subject.

$$\text{speed} = \frac{\text{distance}}{\text{time}}$$

Light travels at an approximate speed of 300,000 km/s. The Earth orbits the Sun at a distance of just under 150 million km.

How long does it take for sunlight to reach the Earth?

1 Rearrange the formula so **time** is the subject.
$$s = \frac{d}{t}$$
$\times t \qquad \times t$
$$s \times t = d$$
$\div s \qquad \div s$
$$t = \frac{d}{s}$$

2 Substitute the known values into the formula and solve.
$$t = \frac{150{,}000{,}000}{300{,}000}$$
$$t = 500 \text{ s}$$
$$t = 8 \text{ minutes } 20 \text{ seconds}$$

You can rearrange the formula for wave speed to make frequency or wavelength the subject.

$$\text{wave speed} = \text{frequency} \times \text{wavelength}$$

The water waves in a ripple tank have a speed of 0.31 m/s and a wavelength of 1.6 cm.

What is the frequency of the water waves?

1 Rearrange the formula so **frequency** is the subject.
$$\text{wave speed} = \text{frequency} \times \text{wavelength}$$
$\div \text{wavelength} \qquad \div \text{wavelength}$
$$\text{frequency} = \frac{\text{wave speed}}{\text{wavelength}}$$

2 Convert the measurement for wavelength from cm to m as wavespeed is measured in m/s. Then, substitute the known values into the formula and solve.
$$1.6 \text{ cm} = 0.016 \text{ m}$$
$$\text{frequency} = \frac{0.31}{0.016}$$
$$\text{frequency} = 19.4 \text{ m/s (3 s.f.)}$$

daydream
EDUCATION

Substitution

When substituting in sport, one player is swapped for another. The same principle applies to formulae in science: variables (letters) are swapped with values.

Calculate the potential difference across the battery in the following circuit:

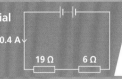

0.4 A

19 Ω   6 Ω

potential difference = current × resistance

1 Calculate total resistance.   19 + 6 = 25 Ω

2 Substitute the known numbers into the formula.   potential difference = 0.4 × 25

3 Follow the rules of BIDMAS to find the answer.   potential difference = 10 V

Calculate the relative formula mass (M_r) of sulfuric acid.

The relative atomic masses (A_r) needed for this equation are: hydrogen = 1, sulfur = 32, oxygen = 16.

$$H_2SO_4$$

1 Write out the formula with the number of atoms.   (2 × H) + (1 × S) + (4 × O)

2 Substitute the relative atomic masses into the formula.   (2 × 1) + (1 × 32) + (4 × 16)

3 Follow the rules of BIDMAS to find the answer.   2 + 32 + 64 = 98

Matt is measuring his reaction time by using the ruler drop test. The mean distance his ruler dropped is 14.2 cm. Calculate Matt's mean reaction time (in seconds).

$$\text{reaction time} = \sqrt{\frac{\text{mean drop distance}}{490}}$$

1 Substitute the known numbers into the formula. $\text{reaction time} = \sqrt{\dfrac{14.2}{490}}$

2 Follow the rules of BIDMAS to find the answer.   reaction time = 0.17 s (2 s.f.)

Straight Line Graphs

A straight line graph represents a linear relationship, where an increase or decrease in one variable causes a corresponding increase or decrease in the other variable.

Straight Line Equation

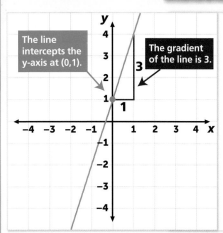

The line intercepts the y-axis at (0,1).

The gradient of the line is 3.

The standard equation of a straight line is:

$$y = mx + c$$

m = gradient of line c = y-intercept

y-intercept = where the line passes through the y-axis

The gradient can be calculated by using the formula:

$$\text{gradient } (m) = \frac{\text{change in } y}{\text{change in } x}$$

The equation of the straight line is: $y = 3x + 1$

$$\text{gradient } (m) = \frac{\text{change in } y}{\text{change in } x} = \frac{3}{1} = 3$$

y-intercept = (0,1)

Finding the Equation of a Straight Line

To find the equation of a straight line, follow the steps outlined below:

1 Find the y-intercept of the graph. This is the value of c. The line intercepts the y-axis at (0,1) so $c = +1$.

2 Pick two sets of coordinates on the line, and use the following formula to calculate the gradient (m):

$$m = \frac{\text{change in } y}{\text{change in } x}$$

$$= \frac{-1 - -3}{1 - 2}$$

$$= \frac{2}{-1}$$

$$m = -2$$

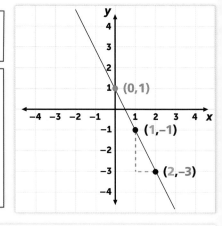

(0,1)

(1,−1)

(2,−3)

The gradient (m) is −2 and the intercept (c) is +1. Therefore, the equation of the line is:

$$y = -2x + 1$$

daydream
EDUCATION

Notes

Notes

Notes

Index

Index